TRE D
CHEST

EXPOSING EXPLANTS
& EMPOWERING YOU!

FOREWORD BY PROFESSOR DEVA

First published by Busybird Publishing 2023

Copyright © 2023 Andi Lew

ISBN:

Print: 978-0-6484584-6-3

Ebook: 978-0-6484584-7-0

Cover Photography: Rochelle Brodin photography

Copy editor: Beckie-Lee of Jazzy Words

Cover design: Vanessa of Raspberry Creative

Layout and typesetting: Busybird Publishing

Busybird Publishing
2/118 Para Road
Montmorency, Victoria
Australia 3094
www.busybird.com.au

Disclaimer

This book is not intended to heal, cure, treat or diagnose anything. It is purely written to inform, educate, and inspire you to look after your own health journey with your chosen medical or natural health professionals. All contributors in this title has donated their stories and work in their own capacity with the same notion.

It is not intended to blame or defame, but rather explain personal stories that have impacted many people and to bring awareness to want may be happening within the health profession. If you have any health conditions that you are concerned about it is highly recommended that you seek professional health or legal advice.

Contents

Dedication

This book is dedicated to all the survivors and 'thrivers' who've had the courage to come out and inspire me to also feel free to own my story in a bid for personal freedom and constant growth.

I acknowledge the man who inspired me to write my first book in 2009, Dr John Demartini; who contributed a foreword. With his kind words, I felt a responsibility to serve and found my gift for healing through storytelling.

My biggest dedication goes to my son, Beaudy who is an oracle. Through him, I see more of me and everything I have taught coming to fruition with his pure vision and interpretation. He knows exactly when to tell me to dive right in and reminds me of the light that I am. Beaudy Shae, you are my beautiful gift.

My parents, Zelman and Terri Lew who are no longer together but shaped me and helped me to love my journey and who I've always been: a creative, sensitive and dramatic being.

I love that we all kept our surname: Lew. In my heritage language, it means "Lev" in Polish and "lev" is "love" in Hebrew. I'm all love and do everything with great heart. I'm attached to my name and we become our names.

To the chiropractic profession, there are so many of you that helped to transform my being into the person

I've always wanted to be. You connected me to my body and helped me to feel safe by removing nervous system interference allowed me to transcend so that I could 'pay it forward' and help others more.

Whether you healed me, taught me, bought my books or employed me, I acknowledge you as playing a major role in my life.

To Dr Natalie Kringoudis who co-authored Eat Fat, Be Thin and Eat Fat Be Lean with me, thank you for directing me to fellow BII survivor, Mel Ward whole kept me stable every time I got scared or sick and held my hand virtually throughout the lead up and post surgery.

To Rosa Milin who nursed me and took me to hospital and picked me up and taught my son how to buy a lady flowers. You were an angel keeping me distracted the night before my surgery and creating a celebration dinner party to remind me that my life was about to transform for the better.

Thank you to Dylan Mahoney who was there and looked after my son whilst I was in hospital.

To Jonathan Moran (JMo) and Jackie Epstein, thank you for writing stories so that I could inform and help others.

To my publicist and dear friend Matt Dilllon, you helped me to grow as a person and created opportunities I acknowledge, brought me to where I am today.

To my dear friend Emily Owens, you listened to me when I wanted to map out my new life, let go of my old one or nurture my creative ideas. I can't believe I met you at CH9 almost two decades ago and we still get to chat most days like little girls playing in the park.

To my diagnosing doctor, Dr Tania Ash - thank you for telling me about breast implant illness and basically restoring me back to a healthy path and saving my life. You are a true definition of the word "doctor", which means teacher. I'm proud to call you a friend too and for joining me in media as we were interviewed on the Today Show.

To my readers, your feedback and testimonials and reviews keep me going. I feel so privileged to help you shape a better life. I love watching your commitment to optimal health as a result of what I've taught you.

Keep the love rippling.

We are here to love. You are love.

Andi Lew

Professor Anand Deva

Foreword

"Listen to your patient, he(she is telling you the diagnosis." William Osler (1849-1919), Physician and Founding Professor, John Hopkins Hospital.

What an honor it is to write this foreword for Andi Lew's tenth book, "Treasured Chest"!

She takes us through what has been a long. difficult. and very personal journey.

In her own unique way, Andi seeks to advise, empower and enable the increasing number ot women with breast implants who feel unwell.

I have been researching these implant devices close to three decades. My interest in breast implants began when I was a junior trainee in Plastic Surgery. A fifty one year old patient was booked for her third set of breast implants after having repeated hardening of her capsules (capsular contracture). The second set had only been inserted four years previously. As we were about to start the case, I asked my mentor why some patients suffered contracture, whereas others did not. He didn't have an answer. That question and curiosity led me on a quest to find the answer that would take me more than 15 years. We solved the capsular contracture issue and found it is due to chronic bacterial infection. Andi Lew came to me as a patient to remove her implants and her thirst for more research and knowledge is like mine.

As a result of our scientific findings and better application and operative techniques, the incidence of this capsular contracture complication has decreased tenfold, but we are still working toward more research to help those who suffer.

Ten years ago, a rare cancer related to breast implants was reported in increasing numbers. Breast implant associated anaplastic large cell lymphoma (BIA-ALCL) then became the subject of intense research worldwide and in 2019, a number of high-risk textured devices were removed from clinical use by regulators all around the world. Once again, good research led to a good decision in the interests of protecting patients. Now our attention is focused on women who present with a range of systemic symptoms who have breast implants. I prefer the term Systemic Symptoms associated with Breast Implants (SSBI, for short) as we are yet to fully unravel all the driving factors behind this condition. Andi is a part of a study group I've conducted and strictly speaking, SSBI is not yet declared as an official diagnosis.

It is our toughest challenge yet but we do believe that inflammation plays a role in SSBI. There are potential psychological drivers also at play. By gathering and analyzing the case studies and developing hard data to derive evidence-based answers, we will get there.

Readers, I ask for your patience as this is complex and good research takes time. I believe the interplay of mind and body act against each other and amplify symptoms in many patients. What is absolutely clear as of right now, supported by research findings from three independent studies, is that women with SSBI benefit from the removal of implants and capsules. These women deserve our attention and our care.

From my very first interaction with Andi as my patient, it became clear to me that she is very much in tune with her body and mind. She combines this with a clear articulation of what she is feeling, which was very helpful to me in understanding the impact of SSBI on her and on many of my other patients. She also taught me a valuable lesson, that we as doctors should listen to our patients. It still blows me away that she was able to pinpoint the rupture of her breast implant when imaging and clinical examination suggested otherwise!

This book will provide a valuable resource for women with SSBI and I do hope that going forward, breast implants, whether they are used for cosmetic augmentation or breast cancer reconstruction are utilized first and foremost with the patient in mind and the patient put first, ahead of all other considerations.

We, as ethical practitioners, need to ensure that women are fully informed, educated, empowered to make a decision whether or not to proceed with breast implants.

For those women who decide to have implants, or who already have them, it should be mandatory that we offer lifelong surveillance for the implants, for the health of their breasts and for the health of their body and mind.

About the Author

For over three decades, Andi Lew has been educating, inspiring and transforming lives including her own constant evolution which has inspired millions. She's an accomplished TV & radio host, and best selling health author.

An Australian transplant living in Beverly Hills, Los Angeles with her teenage son, Andi was granted an Extraordinary Talent Visa as a Wellness & Lifestyle Expert and TV host to continue her work that often takes on a crusade.

It was an organic transition from having reached millions in television shows like 60 Minutes, NY Live, CBSLA, KTLA, Good Day DC, Mornings, Sunrise and Today Shows with the content of her 9 books. This is her tenth title.

She's often referred to as ageless and tenacious and that the energy she exudes is what keeps her loyal audience engaged.

In 2009, Andi won an award from the Chiropractor's Association of Australia for her dedication to the profession in public education. To this day, nobody who's not a chiropractor has ever won this award.

From introducing Arnold Schwarzenegger on his Australian appearances to hosting numerous television, radio shows and her own podcast, Well to Do, Andi is dedicated to helping you live a greater quality of life naturally.

Find out more on www.andilew.com

About the contributors

Dr Tania Ash
Integrative GP, CBD Prescriber, MCAS Literate Practitioner

Dr Tania Ash has 30 years experience in medicine and integrative medicine.

She's been co-managing patients and wellness coaching clients with Andi for a couple of decades and they remained friends through her recent diagnosis of breast implant illness and mast cell activation syndrome which led them both to a press tour to educate others on how to explant.

"I am a clinician, teacher and lecturer of Functional/ Integrative Medicine (IM) in Australia. I hold a medical degree from Melbourne University, a fellowship with

RACGP and a fellowship in Integrative Medicine with A5M (Australasian Academy of Anti-Aging Medicine).

I have worked with patients with complex illnesses incl chronic fatigue syndrome (CFS) /fibromyalgia, stealth infections, mold CIRS and autism over the past 26 years. Curing myself of CFS through my IM systematic approach-including elucidating genetic MCAS (mast cell activation syndrome)- has given me a deep empathy for the many challenges that my patients face, as well as a great drive and commitment to determine the root causes of my patient's health issues.

I have always endeavoured to be the final port of call for my patients by creating a comprehensive management plan, that includes screening and treating chronic infections, addressing environmental toxins and supporting detoxification, boosting energy production on a cellular level, evaluating epigenetics, as well as correcting nutritional and hormonal deficiencies to optimal levels. Balancing the sympathetic and parasympathetic nervous system also plays a fundamental role in rest, repair and restoring the immune system too."

Professor Anand Deva

Prof Anand Deva's practice covers a broad spectrum and includes cosmetic surgery of the face and body, reconstructive facial surgery, elective and acute hand and reconstructive microsurgery. He graduated from the University of Sydney in 1991 with Honours. After completing an internship and residency at the Royal Prince Alfred Hospital, he was admitted into advanced training in general surgery in 1994 and completed a Master of Surgery in 1996. He commenced advanced training in plastic and reconstructive surgery in 1996 and obtained his fellowship of RACS in 2000. He has received numerous awards and prizes recognising his contribution to research and teaching.

Introduction

Transparency, truth, tribulation.

" *The world breaks everyone, then some become
strong at the broken places.*"

Ernest Hemingway

"Your energy is what makes me follow you". That's what I was told in my social media private messages when I created a poll to my loyal fans and followers, asking them why they follow me.

Apparently my energy is contagious. This feedback started making me realize that "wellness" is about a high vibrational energy. It's what I was doing with my vibration that was observed as powerful, so I needed to write this book and share the power with you.

I was getting complimented more and more through my readers who were witnessing my own journey in life, and how I turned trauma and tribulation into absolute triumph. How could I keep that feat to myself? It's only fun when you share a good thing.

I was the most scared I've ever been 'coming out' with transparency, about the truth of who I am, and what happened to me. However, there was a sense of freedom in this. The freedom of knowing that I am doing a better job for you by being true to me. Humans search for truth, and nothing else would have made sense.

You might have read all of my books, or this could be your first. Nonetheless, you will know me well (no pun intended since I'm all about being well) and through this, I plan to teach you how to take care of yourself better.

You may have come to me and bought this book because you want to learn about breast implant illness or you may want to be inspired by my life story. Both of those, or any of those are great.

"I wish I didn't do this to myself", was my inner dialogue when I was diagnosed with breast implant illness. "You did this to yourself" was another similar phrase I heard from the external collective.

In the chapters of this book, you'll see the merging of your inner world and voice, and external world and truths revealed.

You're about to read a book about a woman who wanted to subconsciously and often consciously, stay a child or childlike because of her first trauma. This woman became over ambitious, which was a trauma response, and couldn't find ways to release it. Yet she turned that and several other traumas into shining light.

I honestly felt sick though. Sick in my stomach at the thought of coming out with it all because I was still processing it myself and I feel like I still am. A part of me is thinking this book is prematurely written, but it helped me to fast track my healing so that I could help you too.

Although along the journey, I continually procrastinated. I wondered if we are ever ready? Sometimes you have to just dive right in! I can tell you now that everything is in divine timing and everything is always on track. So when you decide to do anything, it is because you are always on track and you are always guided by divine timing. This is why that skipping rope just kept turning (creatively speaking) and I decided to jump right in and just start jumping.

I read somewhere once, that if you didn't feel scared to share something in your book, then you're not sharing enough. You may resonate with this. What is it that you felt you really needed to do and procrastinated about?

When I owned a wellness clinic for 11 (You will note this theme of a double one) years, I attended many seminars, and one of the speakers once said, "If you don't have one disgruntled customer now, and then, then you're not serving enough people!"

"You're the real deal", I got told by Dr. Ondre who was giving 10 minute energy readings at Soho House, West Hollywood. He said., "I've got nothing to say to you. Let's talk about your son!" This was the first thing he communicated to me as soon as I walked in the glass walled meeting room. It was confirmation and affirmation that I was in alignment and he knew immediately what I'm here to do. What I am here to do on this very planet in this very lifetime is to not play small. We often focus on our past lives or our future lives but what about this life? How are we here to impact? I have always been aware of the very short space of time that we have in this very life and want to leave a legacy.

I know this book will give you an entertaining and insightful read through the wisdom I have collected from not just my own heart, life experiences, and mind, but also from the knowledge of others, that I sought guidance or healing from.

The collection of books and cards I have released now totals 11. This is my 10th book plus my wellness affirmation cards - Calm & Connected comes to 11. This book is one of the most extraordinary books I have written in my entire career.

If you are aware of Angel numbers, you will understand that the 'double ones' or the number '11', has significant meaning. It means you're in alignment when you keep seeing these numbers. You're in alignment with your higher purpose. You're in alignment with who you really are. I've been very aware of my path, but since seeing these angel numbers recently in the past few years, I have really started to take note.

So as you can work out it's no accident that this book is my 11th project. For the past few years, and perhaps, even decades, I have relentlessly stayed in alignment, with who I am as a storyteller and wellness educator. I know it's my calling to move people towards living a better quality of life naturally. And so too, you made your way to me because of the clarity of my being, and we are near reflections of each other.

This book is about emotionally scaling you to a high vibrational being that you are and you have found yourself drawn to me because you are exactly where you need to be right now. We have found each other because we are both resonating in an elevated vibration.

I used to think if I ever told you my story that nobody would ever believe me based on what you see on social media, TV, radio or on stage. One would think that it is all sunshine, rainbows and unicorns. However, as you know, you need to have rain before the rainbow, and I can tell you right now that there were many storms.

And so here we go! This story is unbelievable. But hey, it's true.

I consciously make choices in my life that will continue to raise my own well-being, vibration, physically, spiritually, emotionally, chemically and environmentally or socially, because I recognize that we are all connected, and that my example of who I am reminds you of what's possible and that you are the creator of your own life experiences by seeing the way I am in mine.

This will be extremely eye-opening and awakening to your own power within. By me being committed to turning my trauma into triumphs and staying true to my calling, I get to show you the way home to yourself.

We are all walking each other home.

At the age of 50, I can honestly say that this is where your turning point lies. You can either choose to be free and vitalistic or stay stuck in the belief system and untrue notion that life goes downhill from here on.

So let's bust out!

Chapter 1

Busting out at 50!

"It doesn't matter who you are,
it's all about who you want to be."

Andi Lew

How did we get here?

Transforming into your divine true self is the intention of this entire book but let's start at the beginning. We need to understand history.

Do we have to count the amount of stigmas that have plagued us and continue to do so?

From our sexual preference, to our choice of profession, to how we parent, to our relationship status, from spiritual and religious choices to what kind of food we eat or what labels we give our diet and of course our age, and how the world has decided that it limits you. How many limiting stories have you been carrying? How many labels have you been wearing?

It's no wonder that you were told you were too fat, too skinny, too old, too young, too ugly, too pretty, too privileged, too uneducated, you have a lisp, an uneven eyebrow, your breasts are too big, too small, too saggy, too uneven, you're overtly flat or disabled and you're subconsciously programming yourself with all this and more, based on others perception of you.

It's not even you. You are not anyone's labels or even their perception. This is your life. It's your story and your rules.

Stigmas and labels or other peoples perceptions of you are not who you are, yet you became it.

You became those things through conscious or subconscious beliefs.

So let's unpack how we all even got into this marvelous mess.

And before we think about judgement. Let me disclaim by saying that I do not judge you for any choices you made. We are all only human having a human existence that may sometimes become spiritual too from time to time. There is no judgment because I made choices that I was happy with at times in my life's journey and then I also had to undo some choices and relearn some things. I don't want to regret them because it's all a part of our journey and these experiences and feelings are what shape us. I will only hold you in love. I will love you and meet you exactly where you are.

Tell me not who you are, but who you want to be. Affirm it. And tell it to me like it's in the now, because it is now. You are those things you want right now because it's innately within you as a desire. The choices you make and the experience you're creating are still leading you to where you want if you are intentional and aware and if you're not then it still will lead you to exactly where you're meant to be because we all make the mistakes based on the lessons we want to learn from.

If we have inner dialogue that does not serve us for the higher good, all it takes is a thought to change it. The action steps after that take care of the rest. Just decide first.

Decide your new path now!

Decide it with absolute certainty because it's all about neurolinguistics programming. Your language is important and your cells are listening to everything. Absolutely it's being created through our thoughts that become things.

Just decide and the universe will conspire to make it happen. It all happens through intention and it happens through energy.

Some call this manifestation and others call it prayer or faith.

What I've decided for a long time now is that I don't age. I believe it in my cells. Of course I'm aging slowly but not the way the majority of the world tells us we should age like a disease. The average person lives until 82. What's their quality of life like and who wants to be average anyway? That's another example of a stigma or story you may have carried. Aging is a privilege anyway. Every day you get to wake up and be alive and exist is a blessing to this world. Thank you for being here and contributing just by being you.

Let's take a longer look at age and aging. I'm now 50 years old but I know I have defied age for decades.

The men I date or have married have always been younger than me. The energy needs to match. Whilst I'm open to other ages, it's the effervescent energy I exude that attracts the same.

What stories are you holding close to your chest? Do you hold them dear to you because your grandparents may have told you that you'll also have a genetic predisposition to "x, y or z"?

Yes, you may have a genealogy that is genetically predisposed to something but "x, y and z" will only be expressed in the wrong or 'right' environment.

This is all unpacked in my 8th book, Connected a Paradigm Shift in How We View Health.

However, it's usually at the age of 50 that stigma and story would tell us that your life is about to go downhill. You are supposed to decline in health. You are supposed to be 'on the shelf' and less worthy of love from this age forth. I am 'single and not sorry' as I write this book. This is another stigma I have proven to be all a lie. I toured with my digital dating book across Australia and America with four years of research on dating apps that culminated into #instalovers - digital dating, DM Disasters and Love Stories, that showed us all how 'singledom' is not only ok, but can be fun, healthy, safe, save you a lot of money and bring you closer to your highest self.

I am unapologetically me, as we all should be. I have been showing up as someone that would do the exact opposite that I am told as a statistic or as an average person, is supposed to do.

Why? It's because I need to live in alignment with my values, and I am the one that needs to be in love with me. Being in true alignment with who you are takes a lot of pressure off and contributes to wellness. That being said, you may know someone who isn't ready to remove their implants or maybe that's you. That's ok.

When you and they decide that they are, and that day eventually will come, I'll be right here!

If you have nothing to do with breast implants but picked this book up out of curiosity for self love and my journey, the empowerment message is going to show up for you nice and strong.

So wherever you are in your life's journey, take what you want from this but let's bust out of old beliefs that held us back and embrace being 50 and beyond.

Living wellness practices decade after decade, certainly shows on me.

I am literally living proof that what I teach works.

I've had many hiccups and bumps in the road in this journey. At times it's been wonderfully well, and at other times I have called it, "divine discomfort" through spiritual growth, and the divinity that our souls are run by. Making peace with this path and your past is one of the keys to maintaining vitality and youthfulness. It's in the peace with your path that you'll find wellness and empowerment too.

We all want peace, right? We all love youth, right? We are probably too obsessed with it to be honest.

The philosophy behind Japanese Kintsugi is something we can relate to in this topic. I lived in Japan for an entire year as a 19 year old impressionable young woman. After a year in the workforce at Warner Bros. Movie World as a dancer and host, I took an opportunity in Japan to work for Club Med holiday resorts as a fitness, instructor and entertainment manager. I also worked for Tokyo Sesame Street as a bilingual show host. I lived in Japan for exactly one year.

The Japanese way was really something different to what I was used to. I was at loggerheads with it all when I first moved over but eventually succumbed when I stopped swimming against the tide was when I truly surrendered and loved my time in Japan.

The Kintsugi way is an art of embracing porcelain cracks. We use gold to show them up even more and allow us to be reminded that our scars or our cracks makes us beautiful, and indeed they are, because there are attributes that shape us. Our flaws are our key attributes.

Your scars are your beautiful reminders. Little did you realize that the evolving you, is about to erupt through overcoming life's trials and an explant.

This golden repair teaches us how to work with failure. The glue is made from the sap of the Rhus verniciflua plant, which has been employed in Asia for about 5,000 years to adhere things, initially the parts of weapons. And the concept underlying kintsukuroi was already gaining ground in Japan at the time; it stems from the wabi-sabi aesthetic philosophy, which cultivates appreciation for flaws.

In the following chapters, we will explore a little bit more on why in the western world, we were not privy to this philosophy, and how we saw our flat chests as a flaw we needed to fix. We were subconsciously dictated to by a profession and even by a gender, that we were imperfect.

Of course, a lot of women or people make the choice to augment for other reasons, and you will soon learn that mine is very different. However, this is more of a western world illness than anything else.

I remember the era of the American television sitcom comedy series called "The Golden Girls" where they loved and explored aging and enjoyed their wrinkles, as well as their dating life, as they got older. These ladies that lived in a share household, led a healthy way of showing up in the world proving that life doesn't only go on in an era where divorce was new, but it's also a whole lot of fun. As a young woman, I remember looking up to this notion of breaking stigma and shared living that was healthy.

Then followed an era of female empowerment on another level. Being in your 40s was the new 30s with the popularization of hit television show, "Sex in the City" and other pop-cultures.

The rise of women meant they were feeling empowered in themselves personally, professionally, and even aesthetically. This really took shape with a roller coaster type effect when women really decided to go extreme with transforming their bodies with plastic surgery. It seemed that this type of empowered woman was a little controlled, contrived or reflected a sense of freedom in doing what they wanted with and to their bodies, but so focused on the outside and not really stopping to look inward at what we have all gone through as a gender to that inspired the physical transformation. Did our aesthetic transformation match our inner one? In some ways it did. Every improvement has a psychological effect, but it's a short term 'patch-up'fix. Until we address the deep scars, or make peace with our past and future selves, can we truly learn to embrace our true treasured chest and self.

The beauty industry will always boom. There's nothing wrong with wanting to look your best. In fact it's extremely healthy to take pride in appearance. I'm observing a social cultural revolution of women (including me at times) who have gone 'next level' though when it comes to altering their bodies and at what cost have we done this?

This book as you're starting to gather, is about the explanting, but it's also about something much deeper. Only now that women are reporting they're getting sick from breast implants and removing them, are we all finally playing 'catch up' to being a support or being our best self naturally!

My journey was very different though. Everyone has their own unique journey. As a 'wellness expert' practicing wellness my whole life, I never realized that one day I would ever have augmentation or put anything as toxic as silicone implants into my body. However the problem you'll soon learn I had, became the very thing I needed to connect with. What a shame I had to go through sickness and a rupture and this stress and trauma to get here today. Do not forget or regret though! We are all divine humans having a human and spiritual existence.

When I made the choice to augment about nine years ago, I did this 'something for myself' to empower myself like all other women felt they did. We were also turned into a sex symbol which we didn't mind. In fact, I rolled with it too. I was never a sexual person until I augmented and the following chapters will explain. Don't ever forget this one thing however: We got groomed by society.

I started sharing true wellness on another level a few years ago with the release of my 8th health title, 'Connected, a Paradigm Shift in How We View Health' sharing the message of how your body has a capacity to heal, and optimally function (when you give it the right environment).

I'd totally forgotten that I had implants as I wrote this incredible book that still sells incredibly year after year. I forgot about the implants I had as they became a part of who I was. It's so hard admitting this but breast implants transformed my mental health state and I became a woman that felt sexually empowered and safe.

This was important to me because I never felt sexually safe or free. As a child sexual assault survivor at age eight, I mentally blocked the assault. I was a confused child.

I blocked it out for ten years until I was then one day raped. A man I worked with broke into my apartment and had his way with me.

Fast track to the age of 42, I feel like my silicone implant augmentation made me forget about that pre-pubescent girl and turned me into an "instant / just add water" (or in my case, silicone) real woman!

Just like millions of other women, I also didn't realize the extent of risks and complications on how serious having breast implants was going to be. That's why I did it. It's why we all did it. We didn't have underground hidden Facebook support groups of women explaining their symptoms the way we do now. We didn't have documentaries like "Explant" with Michelle Visage.

So many of us say they didn't feel like they gave true consent because they were not honestly or properly informed of the ingredients. They felt like if they were and they understood what the ingredients were then they may have thought differently about it. This is the new hashtag #metoo movement.

This book isn't going to be about blame. It's not blaming the surgeon or the manufacturer or even the people because we are all just human. However, we will certainly look at why we allowed an entire medical profession and culture to shape our health and how this really becomes a detriment to our health. It'll help you understand it so that you can navigate it better and we can hopefully make the industry change for the better.

I started to understand that the cosmetic and augmentation industry is the only health profession and medical industry that is the only division of medicine that's focussed on aesthetics first, not health.

Yeah sure, a pull towards some kind of aesthetic improvement, can lead to improving mental health but from my understanding the majority of women are having augmentation for a certain standard of female body expectation in western world society.

I remember speaking to my implanting surgeon about my strong psychological reasons for wanting to have the operation in my first consult with him. There were tears pouring down my cheeks as I communicated my story. He said that he was very surprised that I wasn't like the other 90% of the women that he saw who came in and apparently told him they wanted him to make them look like a "porn star". Sexualization of the female body is rife and mine was so much deeper than that.

You'll learn in other chapters, just how deep this psychological reason was, and how it had an effect on all my life decisions, including this one. It got me thinking how many other big life choices do we make that are actually connected to something deeper?

I'm not alone, because only when I went public in the media and social media with my story, after my explant, did I have an influx of women telling me that they felt the same. I was mortified, yet somehow relieved to hear that putting in implants for sexual assault reasons was something others were feeling but it just wasn't spoken about yet.

We all have a story and it can shape you or define you. Again, no pun intended.

I prefer to allow my story to shape me as a person. I fully own that story because it's what makes us so real, unique and beautiful.

I used to let my story define me. I used to let it make me a person that was afraid to step into my true self. Who we are is good. Own it all.

It made me wonder how many more of us have a story that we didn't realise was stopping us from being who we truly wanted to be? I mean, I was already wildly successful, adventurous, courageous, tenacious and had a wonderful life. Yet something was holding me back from absolute freedom.

Think about it in this context. Imagine a person finally 'comes out of the closet' and anounces their sexuality or their pronouns.

Imagine a person that finally shares their disability (mental or physical) and they share that to their crush or colleagues.

Now, imagine the freedom that comes with sharing anything tough.

Imagine being at peace with how the truth really does set you free. Now imagine the beauty from that truth being shared in the eye of the listener. How could you ask the listener not find the truth anything but extremely beautiful?

This is the difference from allowing a story shape you or allowing your story to begin defining you. Define is a derivative of the word "definition", and it's the definition of your story, and it's meaning that can set you free when you change the perception of what the listener or the receiver is coming into contact with.

Additionally, it's all about your delivery. When you have certainty, conviction and love in your delivery is when it will be received with absolute gratitude, and awe. The awe comes from your courage to be so honestly heart led. Others wish they could too. Show them how.

Can you imagine feeling so confident that you actually don't care what other people think? I love the saying, "Speak my darling, even if your voice shakes."

Speaking up and announcing who you are in this world will give you so much freedom. I want you to get to the point where you really don't care what other people think because we need to remember that how they receive us is merely the inner voice they're using for themselves.

Take, for example, when someone is unkind or some kind of bullying occurs. It's usually because there's a part of themselves that wishes they could have the same strength as you. There's a part of themselves that wishes they could be as courageously bold as you, yet they cannot, and therefore usually project their insecurities and fears onto you. Remember this when somebody shares with you, their strong opinion, and it doesn't resonate with you ask yourself if this is merely projection, or if this is information that can certainly serve you or you can learn from it?

Please remember that when you receive any kind of information that is unkind or anything less than empathetic or supportive, then it's because it's a direct reflection of that person's inner voice to themselves, and usually has nothing to do with you.

How we as women started changing our chests is all still sometimes so fascinating to me.

Our chest wall is where our breasts are and it's all so connected to our hearts.

The movement of a relatively new culture of just decades of breast augmentation was all shaped with an ideal of a production line of, if you like, Barbie doll women who are at almost the mercy of their implanting surgeon, when an actual fact, we could be educating them on new beauty standards.

The very first contemporary breast implants given to a woman with breast enhancement surgery, as we know it, originated in the early 1960s, when Drs. Frank Gerow and Thomas Cronin invented silicone breast implants. The story goes that Dr. Gerow squeezed a plastic bag filled with blood in the ER room where they were both working and remarked that it felt like a woman's breast, giving him the idea for silicone-filled implants.

The warmth he felt and the soft, mailable texture kind of made me feel squeamish because I wondered why he was thinking about breasts during another surgery. None the less, it's these men that invented this "solution" to a problem that was projected upon us by their view of what we should look and feel like, or what we wanted them to have us look and feel like? Is it the supply or the demand?

This is where the visions of our surgery production line kicks in for me. Women lining up to be altered at the mercy of mainly male cosmetic / plastic surgeons.

It was in the 1990s, that citizens raised concerns about breast implant safety and silicone material, asserting that silicone leaking from breast implants was causing autoimmune diseases. This eventually led the FDA to ban the use of silicone breast implants in the United States, except for women undergoing breast reconstruction surgery following lumpectomy or mastectomy for the treatment of breast cancer and for women who already had silicone implants and needed to have them replaced.

I also acknowledge the very difficult scenario of women needing a replacement. I cannot imagine how this must feel, and potentially not even the same as losing a limb.

The surgeon that eventually removed my breast implants, as you will soon learn in the following chapters on 20 February 2023, has since explained to me that he only explants, and very rarely will continue to implant for those few mastectomy patients, and even then warns them of the very real risks.

Following the FDA ban on silicone implants, the only choice of implants that breast enhancement patients had were filled with saline, a sterile saltwater solution that the body can safely absorb in case of an implant leak.

Everyone keeps asking me if there's a safer option of silicone or saline. You'll soon learn none (in my opinion) are 100% safe. However, we want to believe nobody would ever hurt us or do anything to us that's risky, but we need to know what we are really dealing with here as we have still so many complications.

How can we have forgotten the risks of contracture where the implant starts to contract? It's the body that wants it to move, be removed and be expelled through an orifice. This is how we heal. We expel toxins through an orifice. There's a whole chapter in my holistic health guide Connected, called "Self Healing Powers" that deep dives into how we heal through expulsion.

So it's not just silicone that we are to be concerned about. We also see and hear many explant patients with saline that have developed illness through mold and bacteria.

It made me wonder why implants are still legal, because so many manufacturers have gone bust (no pun intended), 'shut shop', become insolvent and closed up after countless recalls or warnings and class actions brewing.

There's always a new product or new way, but it just seems there's nothing safe because the human body just doesn't want it and it's eventually catching up to us, playing havoc on our health.

How many more studies do we need? How many more stories of things going horribly wrong before we don't want to take a risk anymore? Will this always be a booming industry or is the time up?

I was a part of a breast implant illness study group by the Department of NSW Health in Australia to get evidence on what this really is. We will deep dive into this in the following chapter.

I understand that we want to improve our looks and hold onto youth, but aging is such a gift as we already learned and you also don't have to age the way we have been told. Remember I'm proof. Let's look at some of the things I've done that are not just mental and emotional practice.

For example, a lot of our body shapes change just through posture. This is why I'm a massive advocate of chiropractic care. I don't just get checked by a chiropractor when I'm in pain. I want structural changes too. When you change posture and structure, and the alignment of an aging spine, you can see that the stomach looks flatter and chests look larger.

It's so much more than just appearance though. I've written about spinal health in my previous books, and how the window to your health is through the spine. This is because of what is inside of the spine, which is our spinal cord and nerves that branch off that it is our entire nervous system. That is our master controller, coordinating every cell tissue and organ in the body. It's through our nervous system, that we perceive the world, adapt to stress, and coordinate all bodily functions. Having a better working nervous system by removing nervous system interference through a chiropractor that is an expert in this, can give you optimal health and communication from brain to body. Nonetheless, we come in all shapes and sizes and that's what makes us so uniquely beautiful but we could all do with a chiropractic assessment. We can all do with better posture and an optimally functioning nervous system.

I decided to journey into and question why I even had to do this operation to myself. I got angry often because 'at what cost' did I change my body that became such a detriment to my health? I mean I inherently knew there were going to be some kind of risks but I honestly either didn't think it would happen to me, or wanted to believe any doctor wouldn't allow me to get sick, or did I not want to investigate the truth? For the most part, like many others, I blindly put faith in my health professional of choice's hands.

Little did I know that getting very sick would take on a huge, spiritual and psychological embodiment of empowerment. I could've easily gone the other way. I could've become a huge victim and become riddled with anger and revenge that would have been unhealthy for me. My anger was healthy. I channeled it into this writing for you.

I realized with all the choices I made in life that all the bad things that happen to you, are always for you and rich in lessons, and that what we do with it can transform or paralyze us, so if you wish to also, take advantage, of turning your trauma into triumph, then keep devouring this book with rapid pace!

It's in this moment that true acknowledgment of my alignment began.

It's in this moment of choice and empowerment that I decided to get revenge with love.

I noticed it's become a pattern of how I operate. It's my gift. I've somehow learned how to turn all my trying times into triumph and inspiration for others. Why did it take me 50 years to learn this?

And now, with this book, I am divinely guided to share with you possibly the most important information you will ever read.

It is through truth and trauma that you can create triumphs!

Chapter 2

**Busting to Love.
Impossible beauty standards
and who's in control?**

*"Grooming takes on a double meaning.
In our quest for beautification,
who truly has the control on how we live?"*

Andi Lew

What happened to me and what inspired me to write this book is profound.

I'm still in shock. It feels like it's a real dream but it really did happen.

I've only just started to realize now that I was slowly dying. I mean, when you're not working on your wellness every single day, we could describe aging as slowly dying. However, this is something different, as I was working on my wellness more than ever before, and in my post operative media interviews, I was quoted as saying. "My body was shutting down".

I had my own breast implants augmented when I was in my early 40s after a divorce that I thought would help me heal from my childhood sexual trauma among other abuse, events and other things.

You'll soon discover why on earth, a wellness expert would ever consider implanting something so toxic, and we may also uncover a little about if we all ever really knew how toxic these devices are.

I had a hole in my left implant bag that six surgeons and an MRI didn't pick up. It was exactly where I pinpointed it was! The most unbelievable part of this was that it wasn't discovered, until after I had the surgery that I had to wait almost years for. My journey to discover that I had breast implant illness, and an

Treasured Chest

Why Andi had a breast 'explant'
My boobs could have killed me

Andi Lew is happy in her natural body after undergoing a breast implant removal. Pic: Christian Anstey

JONATHON MORAN

HER breast implants had ruptured and were leaking into her body, but a doctors told Andi Lew there was nothing wrong with her.

The TV host, podcaster and author persisted and it was not until Sydney doctor Anand Deva removed her implants and surrounding tissue that it was found her left implant had ruptured.

"Luckily I persisted with what I was feeling," Ms Lew told The Daily Telegraph.

"The doctors told me there was nothing wrong, no leak, no hole, no rupture, that I was fine."

Ms Lew, 49, who is mum to a 13-year-old son, originally had the implant surgery eight years ago and while initially pleased with the result, she started to feel ill with various symptoms she believed to be Breast Implant Illness (BII).

Some of the symptoms she suffered included rapid hair loss, tinnitus, structures of breath, anxiety, inflammation and gut and digestive issues.

Some tests showed a "stage two" contracture, meaning the implants were being replaced by the body.

But, despite seeking assistance from medical ex-

perts in both Australia and the US, Ms Lew was told there was no rupture.

"I knew something wasn't right," she explained.

"I had six surgeons tell me there was nothing wrong.

"They did an MRI and nothing was picked up.

"Because I was still noticing was wrong, I had to keep pushing and I felt like I was going crazy. There is a long list of more disgusting things in these implants.

"At some points I even felt like I was dying or wanted to die and it was because literally my whole body was reacting and shutting down."

Ms Lew is based in Los

Angeles and returned home to Sydney for a ground-breaking en bloc and complete capsulectomy surgery at Macquarie University Hospital five weeks ago.

"I was literally dying to be well. I was in survival mode," she said.

"All of the tissue was being pulled away to the area of infection. It sounds dramatic but my body was shutting down slowly.

"At the time of surgery, I had not done a bowel movement for 16 days, which is indicative of my detoxification pathways no longer functioning and not being able to work."

The surgery Ms Lew underwent is a costly exercise, typically about $14,000 out of pocket that Medicare and private health care will not cover. However, if a person suffers a rupture and is triaged through the emergency public hospital system, it is covered by Medicare.

With doctors telling Ms Lew she did not have a rupture, she saved the funds to pay for the operation.

"I love my natural body and I really want women to know that they can listen to their bodies and know that explant surgery can be a really positive thing. It doesn't have to be scary," she said.

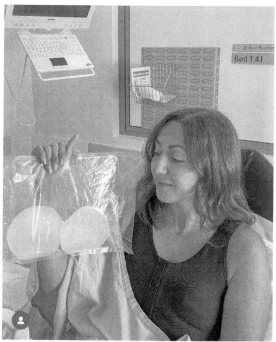

> **I knew something wasn't right. I had six surgeons tell me there was nothing wrong ... but my body was shutting down.**
>
> *TV host, podcaster and author Andi Lew*

undetected rupture, (which followed in me exploring the removal of them) was something that took a couple of years to accept and then feel healed.

In 2020-2022, I was living in Sydney, in Bondi Beach, where I wanted to be close to the ocean and had moved from Melbourne during the pandemic, because I had health symptoms that were worsening. To be able to flee during a strict lockdown and save myself, I also created a job for myself in "essential services" so that I could cross borders.

It was a case of survival, literally.

In hindsight, I have been in 'survival mode' for many years. It's no wonder I've still come out thriving. I guess everything I teach was now really put into practice.

From Sydney, I moved to Los Angeles in July 2022, to advance my career status and give my son and I a brand new life.

We had been living in Beverly Hills for about four months, and I had already been diagnosed with breast implant illness by my Australian doctor but I had not removed my implants yet. We thought we had time. My body was telling me we didn't.

I landed up in a clinic of a Californian surgeon on midday and the middle of 2022 on a mildly warm sunny day, but the sterility of the clinic I'm standing in where I wait to be seen by this American plastic surgeon to seek a new professional opinion, keeps me trembling and chilly.

It's important to me to have another opinion because I'm no longer in Australia and no longer able to see the original Explant surgeon I sought the opinion of. We had a surgery date for the following year but even if I could get on a plane, his wait list was still too long.

Let me address something I learned very fast.

There aren't enough explant surgeons that can perform "complete capsulectomy", which is the special type of surgery that is now done to remove breast implants and their surrounding scar tissue.

This means that there are only a handful (albeit growing number) of specialist surgeons in the world that we can seek the services of. I was hoping this one could help me because he was close to my home in Beverly Hills.

The anticipation of the notion that this is my 4th medical opinion now, and not knowing who's got the right answer on how to get me well, contributed to this crusade, if you like, that I, like many other BII sufferers seek before they explant. I had seen a couple more in Australia to make sure I didn't have a rupture in the implant bag and so I could have peace of mind getting on a plane. I saw another in Los Angeles prior to this day also. He also didn't pick up the rupture.

However, I remain hopeful this time as I cannot wait any longer to be seen by the first explant surgeon. "What if I was dying now?" These were my thoughts and it certainly felt like it. It was hard to describe at the time because it was slow and felt like nothing I could ever imagine my body would feel.

I honestly wanted these bags out now. I couldn't see myself waiting for six months let alone six days. In hindsight, the only thing I could describe this as was "torture".

Moving to Los Angeles was important to me and a result of the visa I was granted: an "Extraordinary Talent Visa" to work as a TV host and wellness expert. This transpired, because as an author, I had been traveling backwards and forwards with the contents of my books on television shows across the country on a press tour, and it started to become an organic next step to make America my home.

It was 15 July 2022, (a day before my 49th birthday), that I packed up my son and myself with a couple of suitcases and we took a great life opportunity to move to the United States of America and start a new beginning in many ways.

This medical visit months later however, is the first time that I would need medical help in the United States. I knew full well that it would be much more difficult than receiving Australian healthcare. Australians are truly lucky in the health care system in that our government has a Medicare system that pays for most of our health care, although it still does not pay for an explant surgery.

Nonetheless, this was a very new experience, as even the dollar exchange made everything in America feel like you were paying double. I didn't have healthcare insurance at this point, but I did have travel insurance.

I bring this up because so many women cannot afford this emergency surgery which is still described as a cosmetic one. Since I went public with my story, I was deeply saddened by how many women are suffering as they wait to gather enough funds to remove their breast implants.

I never anticipated that I would need to be in this person's clinic, as I honestly thought I could wait those six months. I had undergone an MRI to give me the "all clear" before I got on a plane and no rupture was detected. Yet there I was. I was desperately suffering and knew something was terribly wrong.

I write this chapter on 4 July 2023 ironically where I reflect on how privileged and lucky I am to be in this incredible country full of opportunity. God bless America and all the people in it. I remind myself that finishing this book is crucial because this is exactly why I moved my life. I moved to continue moving people towards better health.

In fact, this entire journey led me here to this day, where I am able to share experiences and knowledge and guide you to a healthier path.

In all the work I do, I aim to heal division. I heal the divide between allopathy and wellness, understanding that we need both, but at different times. This was one of those times.

I understand prevention is the cure, but now I was at the mercy of the allopathic model of emergency care. Although I wasn't being treated as an emergency.

Surgeons want to make sure you're doing the right thing and that they're not rushing into the surgery and potentially missing something else. Having said that, whatever you may have going on, having implants exacerbates the other health issues.

So the symptoms in my breast implants were worsening and the surgeon that I sought my first consultation with had suggested I visit this other practice since I was digressing and because he couldn't or wouldn't triage me. Was this because there was no rupture detected in my MRI? Would I have been a case of "911! Emergency- 000!" if it was picked up?

I can't believe that most of these other surgeons didn't even read my MRI. There was a fold detected in the left breast implant which admittedly was there since day one. I reported this repeatedly to my original implanting surgeon but year after year the symptoms and research and even recall of the products were downplayed and the aesthetic result was the main focus.

This is crucial to know because it'll help you understand the profession more and through my story now I'm pioneering change. You'll see exactly where that change was implemented and inspired as a result of my case and now many others too. Surgeons are starting to listen to us because the sufferer becomes the expert.

Let's also understand a little bit more about what breast implant illness is. You will note in the previous paragraph I wrote that the symptoms in my breast implants were worsening. Breast implant illness has been described as an entire systemic response and it has countless symptoms as each patient suffers differently, depending on which organs are shutting down or what their genetic predisposition may be.

More than 100 symptoms have been reported by sufferers. They usually begin immediately after being implanted or years later.

These are a list of some breast implant illness symptoms:

◊ Joint and muscle pain

◊ Chronic fatigue

◊ Memory and concentration problems

◊ Breathing problems

◊ Sleep disturbance

◊ Rashes and other skin problems

◊ Dry mouth and dry eyes

◊ Anxiety

◊ Depression

◊ Headaches

◊ Hair loss

◊ Gastrointestinal problems

◊ Vertigo

◊ Food intolerances

◊ Heartbeat irregularity

◊ Light sensitivity

These were the symptoms I had:

◊ Brain fog and confusion

◊ Food intolerances / sensitivity

◊ Mast cell activation syndrome

◊ Stage two contracture, and the implant sliding into and in between my rib cage with the ribs and clavicle and shoulder, slowly dislocating and going out of alignment.

◊ Feelings of suicide, or felt like I was dying because my system is shutting down

◊ Loss of libido

◊ Inability to breathe deeply

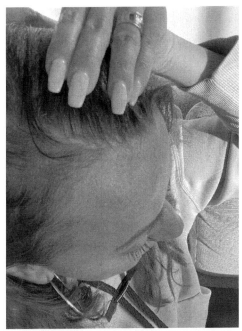

◊ Sleeplessness and night sweats

◊ Anxiety, depression and medical gaslighting telling me that nothing was urgent and questioning whether it really was implant illness or something else

◊ Inflammation

◊ Continual hair loss

◊ Bowel and digestive disorders like small, intestinal bowel overgrowth otherwise known as SIBO / constipation - passing stools once every five days and prior to surgery I had not eliminated any waste for 10 days!

◊ Not sweating for about one year!

◊ Insatiable thirst

◊ Heart palpitations

◊ Anus bleeding

◊ Dry eyes

◊ Tinnitus and brain buzzing which felt like I'm an antenna (heavy metals bouncing around interacting with 5G radiation. When 4G was around, I felt like it was there but not as bad)

◊ Localized pain in the left breast where the undetected rupture was. I had a pressing on the rib cage from week one which I reported but it got progressively worse year after year. I was told it was just a fold.

◊ Light sensitivity

However, this time all the symptoms that I was expressing, was worsening and in a localized spot. It was in the left breast implant along the bra line, but close to the armpit.

Having worked in a health clinic for many years, I knew that cancer is a localized pain that you can pinpoint. My mind kept wandering to that because this is the only thing I could describe it as. I was obviously feeling the fold and the rupture or tear and hole. Just weeks prior, I also felt a frightfully scary sensation of the implant bag moving as it slipped into the space in my rib cage. I was in the shower and felt breathless. I put my hand to the area of pain and felt it inside. I thought I must be imagining it, so I called my teenage son to help me and confirm what I felt was true. He put his hand in that spot for a matter of a second before he screamed and pulled his hand away. This was confirmation, that indeed, I knew what was happening in my body. I grabbed the implant, and managed to lift it out, as though I was putting it back in place. Also note that my implants were sub muscular, meaning they were implanted underneath the pectoral muscle. Previous to this type of procedure, many patients were given the option to have them sitting on top of the muscle. I was told that under the muscle would keep them in place. I guess this is a perfect example of the body wanting to do whatever it wants to do.

I was already aware of the myriad of symptoms that we touched on and will explore further in this book in the following chapters, but this doctor visit was because that left side that I kept talking about, was concerning.

What I was experiencing in that left side was haunting. It was not only a sharp, stabbing pain, a dull, recurring throb and pain, a movement of the implant itself, and feelings of my rib cage, moving as well as swelling in this entire area, and a physical distortion i observed, which is commonly known as contracture. Because this apparent "stage two contracture" was only at stage two, (not three where one looks botched) it wasn't viewed as an emergency.

It seems that the allopathic model is very concerned only when something is very far gone and potentially at stage three contracture where you can actually see the aesthetic changes. It was like stage two contracture was dismissed because I still had a great aesthetic result.

My aesthetics weren't concerning me anymore but how I would be operated on and how I would look after the surgery of course is still of concern. These are the two focal points a patient will work on.

When we go into the operation, one would say we are well, although if we looked at our mental state, I wonder how sound our minds really are going into this.

I continued to see many therapists to help me prepare for it mentally, physically, emotionally, financially and spiritually. It's started taking on a spiritual path as I wanted to stay in control with such determination.

My point is, that going into a consult with a surgeon to have implants removed, is a much harder one than the majority realize because of how unwell you actually are.

Some of the symptoms are the brain fog mentioned previously and the inability to retain new information which is absolutely frustrating since I knew that my well mind normally processed information differently. Couple this with the fact that every surgeon has a different way of practicing or a different opinion of what they think we will look like and this all becomes very confusing.

So let's deep dive into how the 4th opinion / consultation went. He barged in with his assistant and went straight into it and I noticed he didn't introduce me to her. She was standing just behind him and it was as though she wasn't even there, but she was.

In America, every surgeon has an assistant for medical legal reasons, and sometimes this happens in Australia too, but I found it very odd that he went to work and she was just standing there. This is when I introduced myself to her as a 'sister' would. It was at this point that I felt like she would be more understanding of what I was going through, being a woman herself, and that he conducted himself with little social awareness or bedside manner. There were just no levels of empathy.

I was busting to be loved, to be cared for, and to be treated with love and care. I knew I wanted to give all my love to everything that I stood for. Becoming well again when my entire life was about wellness was like telling a cyclist he would lose his legs. How could I carry on teaching wellness when I wasn't well? It was and is my world. Needless to say my income and ability to earn suffered immensely!

How I parent was being impacted, and how I worked was being impacted. This disease started taking over my entire life. I was no longer in control.

During the history taking, it was almost like he was just surprised at my story. This story you'll soon learn in detail. In hindsight, these surgeons are not trained to deal with the symptoms us women go through. It's like they were prepared for the implanting but never got prepared for the ramifications of what would unfold years later. Yet, are they the ones in control of our lives? We are busting to be well, and as I commonly called it at this point, "dying to be well."

For the surgeons, when patients return to their offices with bad news, it's a case of "Wait! I didn't sign up for this!" And also it's a case of the industry and profession almost not even wanting to admit there's a problem. If they did, they would most certainly stop practicing. Or they would at least take a harder look at how they're practicing.

When I entered the reception area, I was highly aware of another woman in his waiting room, with a huge smile on her face as though she was excited to have her implants put in by this man yet I couldn't disrupt her elation, and let her know that there's a chance potentially down the track that she would be like me. I thought of her. I'm an empath and a human. How could I not? I thought of all my sisters on this planet.

So after some time in the room with him, explaining my history and story, and thinking about all the other women, he walked out to allow me to change into a gown, so that he could physically examine me.

I wasn't sure whether the minutes that he left me there, were in fact too long or they felt too long. Just like when you're in love, one minute can feel like an eternity in a first kiss, but this was time standing still in a different way. I walked over to the window to break free from the clinical environment which was a reminder of my suffering.

I tried to find a lookout point outside to focus on but there wasn't one window that didn't have a tiny female torso sculpture sitting on the windowsill.

There were at least four or five naked female torsos that stared back at me as I tried to find some kind of solace looking out onto the streets and away from the practice. These torsos were strategically placed to decorate his clinic in theme, but also reminders of the body that I thought I should have and in the place that wanted me to have it.

Every torso had a tiny waist and hourglass like figure, but they were a reminder of how groomed we all have been for far too long. Why do some women have rounded bellies and some women have thick waists? It's because they're women and we come in all shapes and sizes and all of these shapes are beautiful. However these torsos didn't have flat chests.

I wondered, "Why do some women have large breasts? Why do some have long breasts or breasts that go to the side or breasts that are uneven or one is smaller than the other?" They're just all different shapes and sizes and they are all so unique and beautiful, but where did we all decide that we needed to fix them?

Additionally, breasts are not always meant to be viewed as a sexual object. It still dumbfounds me why in our western culture we are expected to or want to cover up whilst breastfeeding, yet other cultures are feeding openly, naturally and comfortably without covering up.

When I was breast feeding, I had huge challenges feeding in public because my baby didn't always want a blanket over his head. I ended up partnering with a lactation consultant and best selling author, Pinky McKay, a very cool pink haired grandma from New Zealand, living in Australia who I met through the Australian Breastfeeding Association. She told me to say "If you have a problem with me feeding my baby, put a blanket over your head." We used to laugh a lot and she made me realise not only how natural and normal it is to expose a breast during feeding, but also that when the female fetus is being created in a womb, the breasts start as immune cells.

The breasts are so much to a female.

They're immunity, nurture, our femininity and power.

Who has the power? Our treasured chests hold so much power and let's not ever forget what a powerful human we are and why we might think of changing our breasts instead of honoring them for so much more. Isn't that sexy anyway? To me, attitude is the most attractive thing we have!

For centuries, we have been obsessed with symmetry. Symmetry can denote health. For example, when one has a spine that is straight or in alignment with healthy curves, it shows that what is housed inside the spine, which is our spinal cord and nervous system, is functioning optimally, our obsession with symmetry and youth has caused us to create industries that are potentially crumbling now.

There was even a beauty contest in the 1950s where pageant contestants had to be x-rayed in order to show their beauty, which was health that came from within. It was called Miss Correct Posture and ran out of a Chiropractic convention in Chicago in 1956.

As someone who has been having regular chiropractic care for decades, and I attribute this to my optimal health, I look upon this objective marker off health as true beauty. I also hosted Miss Universe and Miss World pageants, as well as a Mr. World pageant for 16 years. They were fun shows to MC, however, as time went by, I always felt at odds with my integrity about being involved in such judgment. Year after year, I continued to work for them, because I encourage the pageant director to allow me to implement Wellness Coaching.

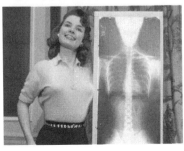

I felt very grateful that I was able to concentrate and focus on teaching that beauty comes from within. We implemented education around nutrition, fitness and posture, which meant the world to me.

I know that I impacted many young impressionable girls who will now be more focused on what their bodies are able to achieve and what they have to offer the world. Your spine really is your lifeline because of what is housed inside the bones of the spine, which is the spinal cord.

The spinal cord is an extension of your brain and has nerves that branch off that. Looking at healthy posture is certainly one beauty standard I admire. Whilst we may be born with such spinal conditions, like scoliosis, and the like, this does not mean that we are not beautiful. It is safe to say, though, I have left the pageantry world.

So here I am. Why did I augment my perfect breasts? You will soon understand my story. A little more in the following chapters. Yet, I'm staring out the window and these thoughts are all flashing into my mind at 1,000,000 miles an hour. I'm wondering whether this explant journey is the new #MeTooMovement?

And now I'm wondering why he has left me here for so long. I was already down many minutes ago, and there was literally too much time where I am left with my thoughts alone in his office.

So I continue to stare at the torsos! After all, it is art to be looked at. My father is an artist and my mother owns a gallery. I always grew up understanding and admiring art. These tiny sculptures however took on enormous meaning. Tears started to stream down both cheeks as

I could no longer hold back the years of conditioning that I started becoming aware of, and that I knew many millions of women wanted to change.

I felt in this lifetime, and potentially many other women's lifetimes where they were confronted with these beauty standards. In this moment, I also realized how much I had evolved and was almost perplexed at how I could have been that person that caved to the social culture of somebody else's ideal.

As I write this story about my consultation, I remember the time where my parents owned a tourist guide publication on the Gold Coast in Australia, and Surfers Paradise was renowned for the beach culture. They often used gorgeous models in bikinis for the cover. I remember being about 18 years of age and asking them if I could join some of the women on their next cover shoot. I loved watching the creative process and as a performer (I was a trained dancer) they may not remember saying this, but I remember that the reason I could not feature was because I was told my breasts weren't big enough.

It didn't matter whether this was said, implied or intended as truth. It was a business they were running and "sex sells" was a common phrase I grew up hearing. It was common culture for cover models to only be those with fuller busts. I wonder how many stories we carry that we may remember or have forgotten about but have shaped our perception on all of the decisions in our lives.

So returning back to me being examined and all of these stories that shaped us up until now, are 'busting out'.

Do you realize how confronting it is to be wearing a gown that is open at the front? It feels confronting because whilst you were being examined, you are absolutely wondering what that surgeon is thinking. Whilst it's completely professional, it's not just clinical because it's aesthetics, and in previous appointments, some of the time these surgeons would say out loud that the implant looked great. "What a great job!" Exactly what nobody needs to hear.

During the examination you are being handled and I remember looking over his shoulder and into the eyes of his assistant. She was a tall, strong and healthy looking woman of color and had a gentle face. As I stared into her deep black eyes, she stared back into mine, and mouthed the words, "it's ok" with no sound coming out.

However, I remember thinking to myself that it really wasn't ok and I wasn't ok. I was deeply sad, rattled, stressed, affected, confused, desperate, and this is exactly why she was trying to tell me that it was. She wanted me to be ok.

I wish he knew her input was more impactful than his at this point. She put me at ease for a brief moment. If only the surgeon used her empathy more. At least he could have learned something from her.

Needless to say, this consultation was one of the most traumatic meetings I have ever had with a surgeon.

The most interesting part was that it had nothing to do with my history, but rather everything to do with how my 'history taking' got handled. He was also aware of my financial position which was strained, but it was like this wasn't important to address. Their fee is their fee.

This introduction to my examination set the tone for the rest of his report, findings and recommendation. He also used a dictaphone recording device to make note of my story, which he very carefully transcribed into his own perception and words in front of me, as he paste like a manic journalist, trying to record an angle for a story.

It is the chill of the room, coupled with his relaying of my story that makes me tremble inside as I recall this experience and wonder how many other women had similar experiences that we simply need to make changes in.

In this moment, I can feel the millions of women that are reading this story and having potential "I can relate" moments. I can feel the future feedback and reviews flooding into my DM's, emails, messages, and in every way I can imagine, every woman wanting to come out with their story, for the sheer purpose of letting go of the trauma and being able to heal it. In this moment, I know that we can change the industry in a positive way and I am hugging all of these women now that are literally busting to love and be loved.

It is actually mortifying that I should conclude the experience and now tell you that the way this consultation ended was with this surgeon writing to my original surgeon in Australia, claiming that I wasn't able to be operated on by him and that nobody should operate on me until I had a psychological clearance.

Telling you this makes me so angry as I recall the feelings of mortification and confusion, that the man and the professional that I went to for help, had rather exacerbated my condition and put an obstacle in front of me. Instead of getting new information about a potential rupture or leak or focusing on what I needed to do to stay stable for my upcoming explant in Australia in 6 months, there was a decision made for me about who, how and when I would be allowed remove my toxic sacks!

I didn't need any more roadblocks. I had been actually working with my psychologist for a couple of years in Sydney and we were preparing for the surgery about a year prior. I was ready to be well. This wasn't helping.

I reached out to her immediately and she arranged a letter that was written and delivered immediately, but I remember crying rivers that night, as I waited for her reply but of course she was in my corner.

It was almost ludicrous that I felt like a man was in control of my choice, my body and my health. Was this a reoccurring pattern that I needed to explore? Was this something I know I needed to unpack with another psychological session? Should the surgeon now be liable for the session I will need to book and go through as a result of his professional opinion that I paid US$400 for? I wasn't able to get this back.

What thought patterns are we all been programmed with? How do we know what feels right or what we are supposed to do when this brand new illness is only just coming to light publicly? How are we supposed to navigate our way through this when it's a case of the blind leading the blind? Or are we blind? Did we know it all already but needed the professional to confirm it? Who is really in control and who is really the right person to lead the one who is suffering?

In my wellness clinics we never called the person a patient because the word means "one who suffers". When they would come in for wellness, they were only ever getting better so we called them "folk" or the people we care for in our community, but even "client" would sound better than a patient. Yet in this instance, I really was a patient and I really was suffering and I wasn't getting any better.

It became very evident that this was not going to be the right surgeon for me. I would need to wait. However, I did go and seek the opinion of two other surgeons in Los Angeles. One was a very strange experience in terms of him not picking up any rupture in my MRI, but he also told me that I would look "saggy" if I didn't have a lift [a secondary surgery] because of my age.

I knew that I wasn't your average 49-year-old and that I had a lot of collagen. I knew that I would look different and so I was quite hurt and upset by his comments but I soon realized that most people don't understand that I'm not your average person. This adjective to describe breasts without implants, felt concerning. I was already thinking, professionally as a wellness coach how many other women would come to me after their explant, feeling haunted by that description of their breasts. It didn't feel fair.

I did not want extra scarring on top of this and his surgery fees were through the roof! I found it so unnecessary to charge so much. For this and many other reasons, he was not the surgeon for me, and so goldilocks (figuratively speaking) went on her way to find the chair that was just right.

The next surgeon I saw after these two Californians was actually amazing. He had so much empathy and his team were extremely supportive. His fees were half the cost, and he suggested to do the surgery much sooner and could fit me in earlier if I didn't have a lift. I considered this but something steered me away. It didn't feel like the right place to have my explant for my own personal reasons which we may go into later.

What I realize now in hindsight is that when a secondary surgery is being sold, it's not just the extra finances that are going to impact on your ability to recover and be well, but it is also the length of time that that secondary surgery will take and how much longer you will be in the operating room, for that may mean you may need to wait longer to be seen. The surgeon needs to find extra time now. At least this surgeon, who was mindful of my finances and symptoms, had made this important for me to acknowledge.

How many women who are desperately saving finances for the operation, are wasting hundreds and potentially thousands on initial consultations? There needs to be a better way that can guide sufferers to the right surgeon for them. That is why I have a section at the back of this book with references and stories of other people who thrived through it.

I learned that by sending my psychologist letter to the original surgeon in Australia that I was back on his schedule. I was now in full control of my health and who was going to be in charge of it.

For this feeling of being in control and choosing the surgeon that I wanted coupled with the ability to recover by the ocean in my hometown of Bondi Beach in Sydney, I decided to try and wait it out.

After all, we were a team and you will soon learn later that my explant surgeon became a very valuable part of my team and healing journey.

I also taught him a lot, and know that he has already started paying it forward to the profession, in a bid to better his profession. You will soon learn some of the things that he was inspired by and how I feel hopeful that because of my case and others, he is interested in making sure that the rest of the profession and his colleagues are practicing in a better way for all of us.

How do we treasure ourselves? How do we take charge and stand up for what feels important and precious? How do I treasure what created us and the miracle that we are? Going through a life-threatening illness operation can make one very spiritual and asked all these types of questions.

It was only later that I realized that removing breast implants is a life-threatening illness operation. No wonder so many of us that go through these have a great awakening. We really must dig to the bottom of our souls and find what is deeply important and treasured.

What we allow is what will continue and this is why I've referred to the movement of women removing their implants as a new hashtag me too movement.

Women are saying that they felt "medically gaslighted". It was fast becoming terminology that was being used amongst online women's forms and in conversations with others in real life.

I've read on these forums that women also felt out of control because they couldn't afford the surgery. So many women are suffering as they wait to find the right surgeon or save up for the operation and some never have success in finding that money so they just continue to digress.

The illness is so interesting because it's such a physical change that makes a deep psychological one yet when the physical change becomes a sickness and it motivates us to remove, the national narrative has sometimes been a case of "you did this to yourself, so I have no empathy for you and you can get yourself out of it too".

How did we get wrapped up into this cultural national narrative, that we applaud women with symmetry or perfection, and our western world cultural grooming of women's torso's? Your own 'treasured chest' has subliminally taken over your own subconscious thoughts.

So, just like the saying that you become the sum of the five people you spend the most time with, subjecting yourself to certain imagery and energy will make you think that what you surround yourself with is normal. But it's not. It's all you know.

Take, for example, all the movies that you have grown up with. What about the stories and fables and animated movies we have been taught to love? Whilst some parts are magical, there are so many parts that have groomed us, since we were little girls to believe that only when we look like a Princess, will a Prince come to rescue us.

What about growing up in an unhealthy relationship or family dynamic? You don't know any other way of being parented and therefore it's very hard to break that cycle when you become a parent yourself.

What if you've been brought up on only junk food and well that's what your parents could afford and told you that you must finish your entire plate before you leave the table because of poverty, mentality and how they got brought up? Ahh, the guilt. And now you're over eating or thinking that eating packaged foods is normal. You don't know anything else. The same goes with those review as our role models or our peer group. If they are around us, and also not necessarily having the courage to really be free, and completely loving of exactly the way they are, then he will also follow suit. It's all you know and familiarity makes you feel content.

You may not have the courage yourself just yet because other role models are not displaying that too, and somehow it rubs off. We become a collective; sum of synchronized beings. It's time to change all and "Treasured Chest" is doing just that.

These notions bring me to question who I really am, and why I've had an inner knowing that educating and empowering others toward optimal health was my calling.

For three decades now, I have helped millions of people across the world, recognize their inner calling, and their healing capacity, as well as their full potentiality as human beings on this planet.

Let me take you back to June 2023. I already explanted in Australia and I'm back in Los Angeles. I am sitting in a creative writer's workshop. It's a rich, velvet red room, traditionally used as a screening room for film. This event, however, is without a movie, but rather our teacher on stage, and some of the most talented screen writers participating. We are in Soho House where I'm a member and I enrolled in this event to become a better writer.

Our teacher, Chela, who resides in Hawaii asks us to begin our class with an exercise that is a conversation where only questions are allowed to be used. It is here that her pure intention and enthusiasm for developing our skills coupled with the energy of all the other gifted storytellers rubs off, and I start to have an epiphany.

How long have I been busting to be 'free to be me'? How many others have been stifled in the story? I am instantly transported to a time I forgot about, but it occasionally came back to me every few years (so it must have been important). It must have impacted me and shaped who I am today. it made me wonder how many others have stories that shaped you, and left on addressed stalled you from reaching your true potential as a gifted creator.

My eyes tear up as I see myself as a pure being that mirrors who we all are, because we are all the same. We all want the same thing: to love and be loved.

It's time we start to breathe as one.

There's so much healing to be done that has been left unaddressed through world wars, and now this pandemic and all of the post traumatic stress disorder and domestic violence that is coming to light. And one of the ways that we can heal this is through creation. It is in our stories and our films and our poems and our dancing or painting an art that we share and healing begins. This is because to feel is to heal. Once we feel the trauma and allow it to shift through our body and release, it is when you can really let it go from your existence and turn it into an experience as opposed to letting it live inside you.

I sit on my comfortable velvet chair and come back to the task as I swallow the tears held back and I take a deep breath. I realized I was holding onto a trauma from when I was about six years old and I watched my baby brother, be photographed by my smoker parents with a cigarette near his mouth, as a joke. They thought it was hilarious in the same way that some people make their children pose with anything adult like holding a beer can or wearing a hat and glasses.

I'm six years old though and in my childlike mind, this felt very wrong and in this memory it's the first moment I realized I care deeply about natural health and healthy living, and how easily that can be taken away with "grooming".

When you are a child, and you observe something, that something becomes all you know, and it becomes your reality.

We only have to look at the works of Edward L Bernays who was employed to groom us. Let's look at his assignments and understand history.

In World War I, he was employed by the government to sell World War I to the public. His Uncle, Sigmund Freud had gifted him, his psychological papers, so he could understand how to manipulate the public. In return, Edward sent him a box of cigars to thank him, and this became his first assignment to create propaganda, which he later coined the term public relations in his next assignments were to sell the health benefits of cigarettes to women and many other things that we didn't need that we thought would make us happy, and thus docile. This was a very clever marketing, tactic and important health history to understand as history repeats, and how we are easily groomed and manipulated to buy into concepts or products.

The mere reflections I observed of my baby brother, were suddenly becoming a dark shadow. The anticipation of my mind races with these thoughts. For it is in this moment that I reflect upon a child in me now, as an almost 50 year old woman, I see my life dedication to wellness education towards inspiring others to be well, began in the early years that shaped me. Or was I already her?

I was never destined to a humdrum life. These reflections are a really loud voice in my head. My breathing often changes when I feel like I can't make a change. That's why this book has been so challenging to write. But warmth came to me in a form of a DM on Instagram last night, I wrote, in my notepad that Chela arranged for us.

In the spirit of this exercise, where we are to creatively write by asking more questions, I inserted the spills of this task into this very book. Read on and know that these paragraphs were from the comfort of that very red velvet armchair.

I used to think my most fearful concept was, what if we don't have time? What if I didn't have enough time to share everything I own you or empower enough people to live their best lives? What if I can't reach enough people? This was half the reason I moved from Australia to live in America so that I could continue to expand my reach.

The DM I received was from a new Instagram follower I have never met. I reflect on how extraordinary the times are that we live in now and how we choose to stay connected and communicate. Social media took over any kind of real life connection from meeting at events and in my practice. Yet the very addictive social media tool that I sometimes despise became a beautiful gift in the form of a message that now notified me of how she found me.

I often ask my new followers how they discovered me when I see a notification like this from someone new. On this day I asked her, how she came to me. Her text replied with a clear and dear enthusiasm that she had been searching on audible, and that I was everything she was searching for. I immediately welled up with tears of gratitude and relief that all the hard work, and all the sleepless nights paid off.

For anyone that has created anything, when you will receive feedback from your customer, it can be the most rewarding thing. For a live performer, you will receive immediate feedback from the audience. Any kind of feedback is precious. I knew that asking quality questions would give you a better quality life and I was so glad that I asked because investing thousands of dollars and hundreds of hours into this audible book about holistic health made me connect with this woman that I may have never had the privilege of connecting with unless I had gone through these difficult things.

She was only one person, but I was sure that there were more. My inquisitive mind and huge heart has already left an imprint on not just my brother's heart, but everyone I cross paths with because just by being me they know that they see my acts of service.

I give so deeply and tirelessly to share all that I know on what's possible, and even though we are humans making mistakes, we chose the parents who we want to learn from their mistakes.

I've always wished there were no drugs, no evil, no darkness, and nothing toxic for us to inject, ingest, or suffer on and wish for temporary joy or entertainment. I wished I had a magical superpower to also never stop aging but that would be silly. For it is in these silly life experiences that we are shaped. They are our greatest lessons and blessings and so the wheel always turns.

We constantly evolve with aging and aging is the gift because wisdom lives there and that's what's so attractive about us.

This is the 'bust out' moment!

This is my realization and your epiphany to accept and cherish your wonderful self as you age.

Whilst removing breast implants is my analogy for acceptance of oneself, this story can inspire your own journey of what you may shed as you really get ready to remove anything that has been weighing you down.

For me, I had a weight loss journey when I was addressing the emotional things that weighed me down when I was 19. I worked at Camp Eden Health retreat and had a rebirth experience. The healing literally took me back to the womb and I remember coming out not just feeling lighter but I weighed myself and I was 3kg lighter! What are you holding on to that you may need to let go of? If not now, at least know this for one day.

For too long now, most of us have not wanted to believe that it is indeed the breast implants that have been making us sick. Whilst some report that it didn't make them sick and I lived with mine for about 8 or 9 years, it's still an accumulative effect. The body can endure so much. It's just that over time there are limitations of matter.

We have wanted to define the sickness as a cancer or a physical trauma. Only recently are we exploring psychological, trauma and injury. We are also exploring multi factorial causes and the layering effect that is a build up of a lack of homeostasis that can cause sicknesses and disease.

We have always wanted evidence and whilst that is still important too, at some point women with implants are going to have to remove them anyway. and so why not do it sooner rather than later? I feel like so many women have not really thought through what's going to happen in decades to come when their explant surgery will need to happen.

You must remember that implants are not a lifetime device, and more often than not, there companies are also going into liquidation because of complications and recalls.

Rather than be reactive and wait for something to go wrong, may this inspire you to be proactive, and take control of the very vivacious life that you have right now and try to maintain that. Allow that these words to prepare you for something powerful.

Removal of breast implants doesn't have to be a victimized experience. The same would go for any kind of unexpected accident, or injury or trauma.

If you could prepare for how you perceive that life experience now, perhaps you could take it on better, and potentially change the outcome for a more successful life transformation.

Ask this one thing - why are you waiting for more evidence or data before you consider a positive life change?

We know that by having a break from sugar or alcohol and caffeine and even technology can improve our health and wellness. Do we need more data and scientific evidence before we go on a detox? Isn't it enough to just have moments in our lives where we choose to remove those things and give our bodies a break?

Similarly, we can apply that same notion to breast implants or anything that may be stopping us from truly thriving.

We don't need more data to support evidence that millions of women across the world are suffering breast implant illness.

They're hiding in on-line groups in a sub culture because they feel they've been silenced, gaslighted or not believed. Manufacturers ultimately don't want us to know.

The testing clearly isn't accurate when detecting ruptures. I had a hole in my bag that six surgeons and an MRI didn't pick up. It was exactly where I pinpointed it was! It's time to start believing the patients and empower them to feel good in their bodies without toxic time bombs. That's what implants are. The only difference is that you don't know when your time is up, and when you do, you can't fit us in!

Medicine is not a perfect science and the plastic surgery cosmetic industry is the only doctor industry that doesn't always have its focus on one's health.

Everyone has a story. Our stories are what make us. They are what bonds us. And through storytelling, we heal. This is because we see ourselves in others and that's because we are all a mere reflection of each other. The more we recognize that we are all the same with the same feelings and thoughts, and, indeed, a deep desire to love and be loved, we realize that all there is, is love.

In this quest of your own healing journey, you must seek the love.

Chapter 3

Loving your scars - getting ready to remove

"The wound is the place where
the light enters you."

Rumi

This quote is deep. It is profoundly true. Light can also be described as love.

You are about to enter a whole new world.

Understanding the process behind any kind of reversal of a cosmetic procedure or re-addressing an old wound or scar is going to be an epic journey.

Whether you are an "Explant Warrior" or know somebody who is, the entire process is actually life transforming, and not just life changing .

Making changes to your body most certainly will change your spiritual self.

The process of removing implants brings up questions around the time you decided to put them in.

It can bring up a variety of questions and issues that are related to yourself, the collective and the entire cosmetic profession.

Getting ready for this new chapter of your life can also make you wonder how on earth we developed such a demand for this cosmetic procedure in the western world.

In the previous chapters, we acknowledged so many insecurities and impossible beauty standards that have led us to this place.

Whether it came from trauma, breast cancer survival or succumbing to the way in which you believe you should look based on culture and the collective, you'll start to peel back some of the layers and have a broader perspective on so many factors that have led us to fueling and funding one of the biggest medical and beauty industries in our modern world.

Once we understand what we thought was once safe and view this as a risky or dangerous procedure in the exact light that it is, the demand will start to diminish. In turn, the supply will lesson.

This is the only way to protect women or any patient and some have communicated to me that they believe breast implants should be illegal. Well, who knows maybe they will, one day.

However, the only way in my opinion I feel that we can create awareness and safety, is to educate the collective (and not just women), and to truly inform the world about this operation and create a world where there is no longer a supply, because there is no longer a demand. There's so many other ways of safely reconstructing breasts. It may not be in the way that we know, but what you would know is that you'll be safer.

I honestly never thought this harm would happen to me! It did.

This chapter covers the practical , physical, emotional ,spiritual and financial readiness one needs to know about. I know. It's a lot!

My reasons for implanting, were such deep, psychological ones that I am so grateful for now fully understanding.

So many of us are only human, and we have our own journeys, which I would never judge. I really tried hard not to judge myself when I made the original action to do it, because at the time it made sense for me, but it became a fun roller coaster ride that eventually caused a nausea that I could no longer ignore. I eventually just had to get off! This nauseating story is full of morals and lessons.

I've always had a deep connection to people who were first here, living in connection to themselves, each other and Mother Earth. Our First People have been storytelling for centuries and trying to tell us and teach us how to truly connect not only with each other and our community but also our planet. They lived naturally and in harmony with all that lives. In Australia they call the storytelling, "Dreamtime".

Yet it's our traumatic stories that have held us back in the western culture for too long. We have sought only happiness as an emotion to aspire to feel, which most of the time made us sad. In man's pursuit of happiness, the exact opposite occurs. So allow me to quantify this statement. What you resist persists and what you fear you attract. You can not have happiness with out sadness much like you cannot have darkness without light and every equal and opposite is in existence always.

And you also cannot silence the heart so you may as well listen to what it has to say. What is it teaching you? How can we reflect and express and communicate better? When will we stop suppressing our sad stories?

I came to this epiphany and realization only after a series of major traumas in my life. I blocked some out in order to be able to deal with it. With the support of a tool box of health professionals, I decided to finally look deeper into them, because nothing goes away until it teaches you what you need to know. The same traumas or scenarios will keep reappearing until you learn from them and recognize a pattern. You'll need to pattern break by being conscious of where it all began.

Have you ever thought of why you keep attracting the same scenario or the same person and keep getting the same outcome. It's all a test. We will cover more about the test that is life, in the following pages.

You see, once you understand that all life is, is a series of events, good and bad, kind and mean, day and night, beautiful and ugly, black and white, you will realize that somewhere in between these extremes is the answer. The gray and the middle in between is always where the heart of love will lie. It's the place where you acknowledge both sides.

It's by sitting in the notion of the understanding that both parallels exist That we can learn from these tests and use them as our greatest lessons in life. That grey in between is the acknowledgment that both exist and in this understanding and these lessons are your most valuable gifts. For this gift is the gift of growth, wisdom, and a sense of peace. And we all want that, don't we?

This is what you'll need to be really ready to remove your implants or go through any life change like this.

Who would have thought that through a myriad of traumatic events, we find peace? So many have shared with me that it was only when they felt that they were dying that they were truly living. You only have to look at the best seller called 'The Monk who sold his Ferrari' to understand that what truly lights us up is man's search for meaning and desire for love and peace.

I often question why humans have to endure such great pain before they can have some kind of spiritual awakening. Perhaps we can? Perhaps through my great pain and in my darkness, I can bring you the light? But then would I be denying you the full spectrum of life and what it has to offer? Why would I deny you any experience of your existence? I say this because with love, I don't want to see you suffer, and if I can avoid it, I will. However, if any kind of pain, whether it's physical or emotional, enters your life, please use this experience as a lesson and a blessing for the life experience, and what it will teach you. Through here is your true evolution.

For as a natural and a maternal being and mother, I always move with great love and wish for you that you would never have to suffer in the way that I did. I know others have suffered too, or so much more than I. It's just a lifelong dream that I wished that we could all see the light without having to see the dark. I guess that's life's huge 'existential bummer'.

The spiritual awakening is in you though.

Healing is experiential. Remember that.

You can't hurry this, whatever this is.

You have to go through these life experiences in order to heal by witnessing yourself come out differently and that's what I'm going to show you I did. I didn't have a typical waiting room experience whilst I was waiting to be anesthetized.

The way I handle the outcome was different too.

I went from victim to víctor.

I'll show you exactly how this is down in the following chapters.

I do not judge those who want to change their bodies with implants or adding anything that may be detrimental to their system. I, after all did it myself. I do wish that I had the kind of support as a person showing up for me that is like me now. I wish that I was her and I could have talked her out of it.

It's ugly and again, it's part of the journey.

Everyone has gone through some kind of a trauma. For some, it begins at birth with intervention, forceps and suction, or even a C-section delivery. Even with a natural birthing process, with stark lighting and cutting of the cord, instead of a Lotus birth, (where the mother and baby decide when to detach when the cord and pulse stop naturally, because we are designed to continue to supply nutrition through this cord) a vaginal, or once thought of as a natural birth, can still be our very first trauma that we as humans experience in this existence.

Trauma can then present in other ways through childhood through the western practice of having your child cry themselves to sleep, or "cry it out"methods of baby sleep training. The reality is that you cannot train a baby, the same way you may train a dog.

The human brain is in three parts. There is the rational, mammalian, and reptilian brain. The mammalian and reptilian parts of the brain doesn't fully integrate, and become one brain until about the age of five or seven.

This means that when a baby is crying, they are thinking with their primal parts of their brain, and not the rational parts the way we do as adults.

This is why that phrase goes "Show me the boy until he is seven and I will show you the man."

It is during this time that you are neurologically programming your child and through traumatic events, such as crying themselves to sleep, (because of the above reasons, which appear as stress) you are not allowing for optimal neurological pathways to develop.

There's simply too much cortisol, which is the stress hormone being released during these crying phases.

This is something I learned from some of the greatest PhD scientists in parenting and sleep in a book called. 'The Science of Parenting" by Margot Sunderland. I have written about it in much more detail in my second book after I had my child and that is called "The Modern Day Mother, babies, and sleep from womb to one".

You see even though we have changed as a species and we live in big houses that are safe, the way in which the human brain develops has not changed. That baby really does not know that a big lion is going to come and eat it. It eventually stops crying because it is too traumatic to continue to call for you because there is an excess amount of adrenaline and stress hormones being released, and the baby eventually feigns death just like in the animal kingdom. They lie there and shut off their deep breathing, staying very still, so that no animal will come and hunt them down because it is their way to help them feel safe. This is the primal, survival instinct. That's their survival mechanism. They literally shut down and stop crying because you won't get them and also they are protecting themselves from the wild.

You may have thought that you have trained your baby to sleep but they are usually just now emotionally unavailable and top lactation consultant, and best-selling author; Pinky McKay refers to it in her books. I was privileged to be able to come across her work when I was breast-feeding and was able to feel supported by her teachings so that I could help my son feel supported and have optimal neurological development. She then went on to write the foreword to my second book.

So if this is our potentially second early childhood trauma. And we haven't even begun our lives yet, can you imagine how much reprogramming on a cellular level we need to be doing to help us really heal generationally?

I started to join the dots, and because I was privy enough in my wellness work to come across the greatest educators and practitioners in all areas of health and wellness, I discovered such healing modalities like chiropractic, kinesiology, and neuro-emotional technique (N.E.T chiropractic) which all work to take pressure off the nervous system and allow it to reset.

The nervous system has a memory, and that's why we often go into a boxer's stance or a position in defense posture when we feel trauma because when we feel an attack, we literally are created to have less blood in the brain and it all goes to the extremities. This stance allows us to run away from that lion or wrestle it to the ground. This is how we are hardwired and programmed to behave when we are in primal instinct. It's a healthy way to release those stress hormones. With our modern-day world however, we perceive stress and are usually sedentary.

We are literally not thinking clearly when we are in 'fight or flight'. This is why when you have an argument with someone you care about and you feel bad about it the next day, and you tell them that you were sorry for saying mean things, and that you weren't thinking clearly, it's because you really weren't.

You didn't have blood in your brain like you would in a relaxed state because it was all in your extremities. You won't notice that your neck also cranes forward when you're trying to get a point across and this is the defense posture. It's about allowing yourself to understand that you are in a safe space and you will be able to communicate more effectively or choose to walk away gently and save it for another time. You may require to use that adrenaline and go for a walk, run or jog. You could dance, surf, make love or do whatever movement you feel. This could be a more productive use of that stress hormone called adrenaline.

And so this understanding of trauma, allows you to visualize the pattern that you have learned when you're next faced with more trauma, or if you are not releasing it, how you may attract it again in your life.

I sit out on a journey to change the pattern, but I didn't always have complete success, or freedom within myself, because as you know, life really is a journey.

This book is about helping you to recognize where something may have been a traumatic event for you and how it may be holding you back from being everything you've always wanted to be.

It's not only our in a dialogue that needs to change, but it's where it came from. It's the stories and narratives we have been programmed with and it's also the stories that are living in your cells, tissues, and organs that you haven't consciously or subconsciously unblocked or released. Perhaps you aren't even aware of it.

Sometimes, even though you may have thought that you removed and released something, it still subconsciously lives in a part of you that you are completely unaware of. This is where I found that physiologically removing the blockages with kinesiology, chiropractic, and neuro-emotional technique really complemented the psychological and counseling work that I was already doing.

The other kind of work that you may like to explore is journaling and indeed storytelling.

It is through our writings and reflections that we are able to see and express what is really going on for us by internalizing our thoughts. Most of the time we aren't even aware of our thoughts.

Our thoughts become things. It is crucial to change the narrative by changing your thoughts too. Most of the time your thoughts are allies. The good news is that your thoughts can be changed.

As I write this book, I am often transcribing it, not just typing it. By transcribing, I am able to walk at the same time which allows me to release some of the energy that builds up if I feel any kind of stress as I re-live in re-tell. So this is my voice to text (or maybe one day you will be listening to my audible or perhaps you are now?) as this information is transcribed and I am walking fast.

This is another wonderful way to download any happenings of your day or life. You may like to journal by recording your voice to text. So many people do it on an online social media platform and they share it with the public. Whilst this is good to engage on a very real level and be candid, I feel like sometimes when you know that nobody is listening, you can create a safer space for yourself to really get honest and know that this is only for you. Then you can internalize it and decide if you want to share it on a public platform forum after this.

Sometimes when you recall something traumatic, you will relive it, so again you need to be aware of the things that may come up for you that may feel like a stress response. Your body will want to naturally move.

I walked past a shop window during this writing process, that had a blanket with the words, "You are loved", and so l I see that as a sign. That's because everything is a sign and everything is meant to be.

You bring about what you think about. With your thoughts which are energy and everything is energy. You are literally bringing into existence everything that you are, everything that you say you are, and everything that you think you are.

Understanding that nothing is a coincidence and yet everything is happening 'for you' and not 'to you', will also help you to start to love your fate.

There is a saying or famous quote called "Amor Fati" and the Latin meaning is not just to accept your fate, but rather love it because you know that everything you are and everything you do and everything that has happened leads you right to where you are now which is where you're meant to be.

How do we know this? Because it already happened. And it also led you to reading this book. It led you to me. And through my trauma and wisdom gained, I feel called to pass on what I know can help you to feel finally free.

This leads me to this new chapter of my life which I call "free to be me"!

Trust me, I have self doubts too, even though I am a best-selling author and have so much success under my belt. Whether it's online trolling or ghosting, (which I actually ended up writing about in the book prior to this one), called "Where'd They Go?", the human psyche wants to understand their own place in this world. Through this journey, I didn't realize my own personal power. I thought that the events that happened were because I wasn't worthy or didn't deserve the things I really wanted. I see now that my light is so bright that it was blinding for others that couldn't shine theirs.

There's something called projection. This is actually a projection of that person's inner dialogue. It's their inner voice to them selves. We must continue to wish them love who we are as powerful and continue to shine in the heart that it will inspire them to have the courage to do the same.

So becoming "free to be me", was as a result the last traumatic event after a series of traumatic life events, that I experienced. This was the breast implant illness, and an undetected rupture in my implant that I had been carrying for a number of years without knowing (because those six surgeons and the MRI didn't pick it up). I need to reiterate how incredibly frightening back in hindsight because I really was slowly dying.

Even the plane flight back to Australia to have my surgery, was a task. On the first flight, I sat next to a lovely older woman. She had a pacemaker on her heart. She told me that she gets irregular heartbeats. I asked her when it began. She said "just out of the blue recently when I'm sitting on the couch, doing nothing strenuous, or in particular." Why is this a difficult conversation? It's what she then revealed to me next has never left me. She was very proud when she discovered that I was a wellness coach and wanted to show off how she recently lost about 30kg. She said that her skin became very loose as a result of losing the weight so fast and her medical doctor told her that she needed breast implants to fill out that skin. This woman is in her 80s and she was doing well to lose that weight, yet shortly after augmenting she landed up with heart issues. Irregular heart beats and fluttering was something I experienced towards the end of my implant illness journey. I haven't had them since.

Oh, the next part of my plane ride was really scary. As we were descending on my second flight, I was in

95

excruciating pain on the left side of my breast. My whole underarm was flaring up with inflammation and where my rupture was, was excruciating. I held my breast and close my eyes and tried to block the pain away. I couldn't quite understand what this pain was because all the surgeons told me I didn't have a rupture. Shortly after, a flight attendant came up to me as she saw me like this and asked if I was OK and I told her that I am going back for this surgery. She told me that pressure as the plane going down was pressurizing my implant. In hindsight, this was so highly dangerous.

Another highly dangerous act is to enter a sauna. Whether it is an infrared, or a traditional sauna, these implants are not tested in extreme heat, and now many surgeons are saying that they are literally melting in your body. I remember having saunas towards the end, and didn't feel great at all, but I was trying to sweat the toxins out of me, Instead, I was creating more.

So finally persisting with my intuition and being in tune with my body, having finally had it removed, we did discover the hole in the bag! It was indeed leaking, and you will see in the pictures of me holding the bag that the left one was much smaller and saggier because it was emptier. Where are all of those toxins now?

When you have the specialist surgery to remove these implants, there is a particular way to do so that encapsulates the bag within your surrounding scar tissue.

There's two reasons that this is important. This type of surgery is called Complete Capsulectomy, or Total

Capsulectomy and others, call it En Bloc. We will dive into this surgery explanation in the following chapter.

1. Your body creates a scar tissue that surrounds and encapsulates the implant bag. If you do have a rupture taking out that scar tissue intact with the bag, it will keep any potential leak contained. It literally will stop the spillage from entering the rest of your body.

2. The surrounding scar tissue is now being tested for new types of carcinoma's. Leaving that scarred tissue inside your body is essentially leaving cancer in your body. The scar tissue is usually sent off to get tested and you will get a report from your surgeon to let you know what to do next.

I was so nervous that we might find something sinister in or after my surgery that I asked my surgeon prior to the surgery. What would happen if we had found squamous cell carcinoma, which is the new type of cancer in the tissue. He replied, "Then we will deal with it!" And you know what? Everything is regenerative, and everything is reversible and people do have miracles every day.

Oh, I kept this close to my heart and chest and remembered that with the work that I do in wellness that it wasn't a prognosis or I wouldn't allow it to be my label.

So often when people are given a prognosis, they live it out until that very day, as if it were a death sentence, telling them that they have 'X' amount of time to live. I would not be that person even if we did find something. I knew I would do everything in my power to create homeostasis again. And besides, miracles happen every day.

With all this in mind, and the weight literally off my chest, I finally felt "free to be with me". I am putting this in inverted commas, because I literally feel like I'm coining this term. I knew I always wanted to be this woman that I am now who is brave and vulnerable and strong and powerful, but soft and family and most of all I am free.

This is a story about the tragedy of that event that transcended into me and having to heal all the traumatic events in my life. It's just that this one was the crescendo experience that was like a light bulb literally smacking me awake with light and love.

Get yourself out of that victimhood and become a victor!

Create this first by changing your physiology. This goes hand in hand with the thought processes.

You probably don't realize this, but any kind of spinal misalignment and poor posture will put you in a defense posture and physiologically, may make you feel more fearful, or less well, or might even just put you in a state of not functioning at your optimal.

It's not just trauma that can put you into a "fight or flight" but it's our modern day sedentary and stressful lifestyle that can also put us into this posture where our bodies physiologically perceive that we are in an even though we are not.

You only have to look at people (like us) who are on technology all day every day to see how they (or we) have developed a forward neck posture, or a "tech neck hump" at the back of the upper cervical spine, to see how this affects our holistic health.

You see, our physiology changes our chemistry, and then in turn our emotional status.

You don't see depressed people walking around with fabulous posture!

When we change our posture, we change our chemistry and in turn, our emotional status changes too.

This is why, when you are working towards turning your trauma into triumphs, you must also work with the physiological body as well as the mind because they're connected. That's because what's housed inside the bones of the spine is the mind! The spinal cord is an extension of the brain.

This is exactly why I enjoy being a chiropractic advocate. Chiropractic care can be a huge assistance in your ability to fast track your healing journey.

Some chiropractors are great scientists and great healers, but they are not necessarily also great communicators.. You can't be good at everything, right?

That's why I like to help the chiropractic profession because it is one of the most misunderstood professions in the world. It also doesn't have the same marketing budget as the pharmaceutical industry does. How could any healthcare profession even compete with that and they're messaging for advertising?

Chiropractic is one of the fastest growing healthcare professions in the world that doesn't use drugs or surgery. There's just too many myths and misconceptions. Perhaps through professional jealousy, people have held off going to seek the services of a chiropractor, but you will soon learn that when you address your spine with a chiropractor that is an expert in nervous system health, you will need less drugs and potentially not ever need surgery.

So chiropractic care, chiropractic philosophy and wellness lifestyle practices can keep you out of "fight or flight", and on less medication, and looking and feeling well.

I have been seeking the services of a chiropractor in many different types of chiropractors for about 25 years now. I have regular chiropractic adjustments and checks weekly and fortnightly. I don't wait for a headache to come. I make sure that I am in alignment and functioning optimally for other reasons that are more wellness related.

If it wasn't for chiropractic care during the diagnosis of my PTSD for other traumatic events that occurred in 2018, I probably would have landed up on a myriad of prescribed drugs that never would have addressed my root cause. As a result, it would've only created additional health challenges as there may have been medicinal side effects if I had chosen the drug route.

There's nothing wrong with using western medicine for emergencies or trauma, as that's when it's designed to be used, but keep in mind, it never addresses the root cause of any health issue. So ideally, it is best to address your health naturally, where possible.

You see, taking medication destroys gut health flora and fauna, which is the good and bad bacteria in your gut.

Medication also destroys the tissue or lining of the gut, and so because our gut is our second brain, we then need to work towards healing two things.

The first one is the one we set out to address originally (the symptom) and the second one is the damage that the medication caused to our gut and nervous system or potentially hormones too.

Now you have two issues to address. You have the reason for your illness that began and then the effects of the medication.

This is why doctors prescribe probiotics after a round of antibiotics. Healing the gut and nervous system after medication takes so much more than just probiotics but it's a good start.

There is so many things that can cause a defense posture, and put you in a 'fight or flight' trauma state. They are physical chemical, and emotional reasons. There's even environmental stressors.

They all impact the nervous system and it's through our nervous system that we perceive the world, adapt to stress and coordinate all bodily functions. What protects the nervous system are the bones of the skull and the spinal column / bones which are your vertebrae.

When you have nervous system interference, you are in misalignment physiologically, and there is no longer a protection of your spinal cord and nerves that branch off that which is what the vertebrae is protecting. It is actually now a distorted signal to your body.

Chiropractors are the only experts in the world trained to detect and correct vertebral subluxation.

Chiropractic is safe, scientific, specific, and the intention is towards correction so that you can have healthy communication from brain to body.

This is why chiropractic care is crucial for anyone that wants to be able to not only get out of 'fight or flight' posture, but also for those who want to have a body that is functioning optimally.

I've been having chiropractic care for about 25 years on a regular basis and I will say that it is the one thing that has definitely kept me vitalistic and functioning with clarity.

Though all the traumas I have had in my life were starting with the physical like our bumps and falls when we learn to walk or perhaps it was my birthing process itself, or perhaps my trauma also began with "cry it out" baby sleep training methods? Perhaps it was also not just the emotional stressors, but physical stressors like my first car accident with whiplash or high heels and sedentary posture from being on tech as I grew up and got older?

It became more and more apparent that this was affecting my posture. For most of us, you can see that these may affect you too. I believe that the most traumatic time for me is a series of events that happened every decade or so for many years. I decided only with the diagnosis of breast implant illness and mast cell activation syndrome (which you will soon learn is the same thing), that I began to heal all of my traumas so that I could break a pattern.

The pattern breaking was a part of perception that I could move through life, not trauma free, but just not attracting the trauma or drama because I'm no longer focused on it - consciously or subconsciously.

I'm now aware of signs and signals so that I can handle things differently or walk away from them.

It's linked with my knowing of how I'm here to serve. We are all here to serve others. We find ourselves in our servitude to others. It's like I didn't have time for anything that didn't help with my servitude anymore because it pulled me away from the limited time that I have to make that impact.

Another analogy would be like if there was a teenager in a schoolyard and he or she or 'they' were about to be bullied and when a fight or nastiness escalates, they choose to walk away.

They've been taught to handle things differently and be aware of when to break a pattern.

The pattern may begin from conditioning from how we were brought up and how our parents were brought up and how their parents were taught to behave and act. It's also a social, cultural, behavioral instinct, which I am so excited about making change to.

Gone are the days where we were taught that if we were in a fight, to fight back. I believe we are getting better at reflecting and communicating.

From what I've read, researched, and observed, I can see that we can create a new world of empathic humans.

It's with true empathy that we create the most wonderful love, human connection, and creation. The world needs more empathy. You're going to need a lot of this in your request of getting ready to remove. Lots of anger and confusion, and all the emotions do come up prior to an explant.

Sometimes unhealed trauma presents as someone who lacks empathy, because if it wasn't given to them, then it isn't going to be normal or easy for them to pass it on to others, unless you've done the deep work. Unless of course you are a more evolved human - evolution begins with us.

Just like writing this book., I wanted to rush and get this out there. I had so many people send me messages, emails and social media posts, sharing my story and answering to my story and telling me that I saved him and that if it wasn't for my television appearances that they would not have gone to remove theirs. I had to evolve and keep healing and this couldn't be rushed.

I remember one lady in particular who sent me an Instagram DM, just two weeks after her explant telling me that she saw me on television a few weeks prior to her booking the procedure and she finally was able to join the dots. She realised what her symptoms were and so she rushed herself to surgery.

It was only after surgery that she discovered a ruptured implant that was absolutely desiccated and green. She told me I saved her life because she didn't know that this was something to question until she saw my interview.

Hearing feedback and stories like that, and seeing the picture of her removed, ruptured and green implant made me want to rush to release this 10th health title.

Every time I try to finish this book, I felt triggered though and had to take a break because I am still in my own healing journey, and so many of us are still learning, (including the medical profession themselves who are searching for more data to prove this danger and risks, despite manufacturers, telling us that it is OK).

Thankfully, we do have some data now being presented with published papers from the likes of Professor Anand Deva who did my explant surgery. It was shortly after my operation that he booked himself a flight to Miami, Florida, to present this new published paper to his peers about the breast implants being the inflammatory driver. I am so grateful for his contribution to this book that you will read in the next chapter.

He and I already knew of dangerous risks that implants create however, even his peer group and the profession,needs published papers so this was a huge win.

Here below is the information that was shared. It will be after the stories and research that you will now consume, which will may make you want to also rush to remove.

Be prepared.

This book will help you to prepare in a way you never knew you needed.

I am essentially "paying it forward" with the knowledge that I was privy to.

In the following final chapters, you will learn what to do and how to guide yourself practically too now.

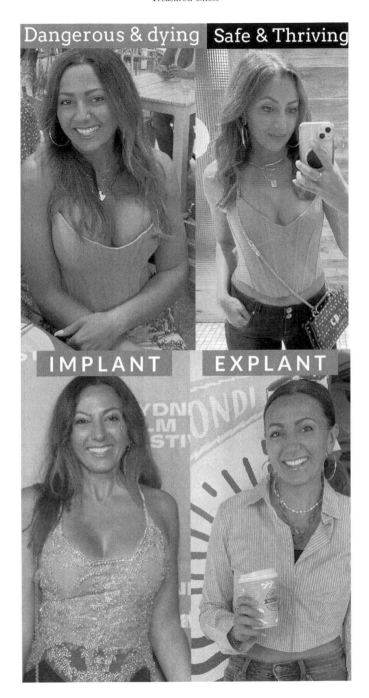

Perhaps learning this is for someone you know or perhaps it's a spiritual awakening of some sort, as a result of your own personal trauma and epiphanies.

Some of the things you read, you'll want to rush to implement but sometimes you simply can't. It is my aim that there will be enough surgeons and support for us to be able to safely and quickly remove, if we need to or choose to explant with haste.

We get choose the timing of our surgery instead of being again in the hands, and at the mercy of these medical professionals that I try to fit us into their very tight schedules.

It's all part of the process though.

I want to save you from some pain but I can't always. Hopefully this book helps you understand what you can control and what you want to surrender to.

Chapter 4

Trauma to Triumph

*"No experience is a cause of success or failure.
We do not suffer from the shock of our experiences,
so-called trauma - but we make out of them
just what suits our purposes."*
ALFRED ADLER

As I write all of this though, I still cannot believe that not even six surgeons and an MRI (which is the highest detection equipment we have), could pick up the hole in my left breast implant, exactly to where I was pinpointing it was!

How many times have I repeated this phrase? Will it ever leave me? Why didn't anyone believe me? Do we need better detection equipment? Do we need to start trusting our bodies or listening to the patients more?

Through this illness, like all illnesses, it can cause you to start listening to your body and use the symptoms as the sign. We are so conditioned to turning off and switching off our symptoms with drugs, medications, alcohol, shopping, sex, addictions of any kind and even self harm because we just want to switch off pain and make it go away.

This story of implant illness paints a picture of how crucial it is to tune in to your body and really listen to what it's telling you. Can you imagine if I believed everyone for another few years and didn't address the pain I was feeling? It taught me to persist and not drown out the suffering any longer to really find out what is going on. In this act, it solidified the message that I teach about wellness in that your symptom is always the solution. It's a solution to helping you find a path to get well. I think, numbing ourselves with these substances for acts I just listed is very dangerous to our overall health.

It's been so triggering to finish writing this 10th book but as you're reading, I know that you're halfway through and this gave me a feeling of happiness because I know that you already are starting to think differently, and I am helping so many people to learn how to take control of their health and bodies.

A part of me will always be in shock that this even happened to me. I am equally as in shock at how many others this has happened to. I have been angry, mortified, sad, confused, and moved enough to create this information portal and support group movement that Treasured Chest is.

I have decided to write the way I would coach any other client in the act of journalling. Writing is a cathartic release with the ability to reflect and turn those negative emotions into processing and releasing. It is why at this point I actually solicited on my Instagram for others to contribute their stories and share them too.

Not everybody has the ability or know how to write their own book. Some also didn't have the desire. However, I wanted to include all of you so that you could feel heard and I have added in your stories as you sent them in. There was no screening process because everybody's story is valid. You matter and you need to be heard. I am sure that this small collection of stories will continue to grow in a published medical papers, in the news, segments, documentaries, films, poetry and songs, and we will hold space for all of you to feel held and heard. Half the healing is in the hearing.

A wonderful friend who is a birthing Doula got in contact with me after years of not being in touch when she saw my interview on the Today Show.

I found it so beautiful that a person that holds space for others during natural birthing had asked if I had someone that would be holding me during this healing and recovery phase.

So many other implant illness survivors and thrivers feel left alone after the operation. But it does not stop there. Their journey continues. Just like women have to care for everything because their biggest life. They have communicated that nobody warned them of the breastfeeding part, which was equally as challenging. I guess one could draw an analogy on how the explant journey goes too, because making it through the operation is like birthing. Or should I say rebirthing?

Nonetheless, adjusting and rehabilitating and the continuation of the healing keeps on going long after the operation and you will need a wonderful support team just like the Doula might suggest a lactation consultant.

In the following chapter, I will create that support for you, and there will even be a resources page at the back of this book so that you can continue to find your support tribe.

Despite all my frustration and grieving and sadness or anger, I knew I needed to move through and past these emotions, so that I can turn my trauma into triumph for others. I have been coaching many after their surgeries, and I have noticed that they to really heal and move past what they feel was frustratingly traumatic but this at peace practice was crucial.

So here's what I want you to do if you have had success in removing your implants.

◊   Find a support network or person

◊   Change your perception about what happened so that you can create change for others

◊   Journal or document it so that we have the data and it is recorded

◊   Share it with others and anyone who will listen to you

◊   Allow yourself to have down time. You're not having a down day. You're having down time.

◊   Discover a detox protocol that works for you

◊   Create. Some have turned to creation of any kind of arts but mostly what can you create that will help you to support you and others?

This is the light I bring to you to teach you how I really manipulated the outcome through my perception of the events and a conscious decision around how I made this narrative work for me.

The more spiritual part of me knows that it all happened 'for' me, so I could help you. This is the bittersweet symphony.

It's what I feel I was chosen to to do. I feel happier when I'm helping others so in some strange way, you're helping me too.

So let me finally tell you my traumatic story that I finally released.

Let's dig deep and allow me to bravely and boldly share my personal life story so far so that you can view me as both blessed with unfortunate events and also blessed with an ability to become triumphant.

We all have this within us.

You may see it in a top performing athlete that just refuses to give up or back down.

You may notice it in a brightly burning candle that you hold for someone that refuses to be blown out despite the wild winds.

Let's start with how I discovered I had to get ready to shed and remove my breast implants.

In 2022, when I was first told by my diagnosing doctor, Dr. Tania Ash, that I had breast implant illness, I didn't want to believe it. Like many others, we became so attached to the implants. They become a part of us, and we forget they're inside us, so it can be a real journey to get ready to remove!

You may be reading this to get ready to remove or if you already have removed your implants, you may resonate with everything I'm about to share.

If you know someone who has implants, may I suggest that you keep a close eye on them, and their health, so that you can start to join the dots and help them stay well or get well.

I was so attached to my implants because of the story that came with why I put them in.

There was actually nothing "wrong" with me to begin with. We are all aesthetically perfect just as we are. We covered that in previous chapters. So I was perfect but I had a history of child sexual assault.

It was something that I had pushed away for decades. Every now and then, I'd muster some strength to reopen the cupboard and do some more inner work but it was exhausting after many decades so we ebb and flow with what we can handle.

I was sexually interfered with when I was eight years old. A family friend was babysitting me, and he interfered with me in a way that I have never forgotten. As an eight year old, it was pretty hard to process because I didn't talk to anybody about it until about a decade later.

At times, I wish to downplay the story because I wish it wasn't something that affected me or was an actual event that couldn't leave me. Sometimes people want to know details, but I will not go into detail in this book. It hurts too much and it also doesn't matter.

All you need to know is that anybody's event or story if it troubles them, there is only so much that their soul can handle, and there are so many reasons why it may affect some and not others. It could be their age or the type of support or lack of support that they had at the time. But even me having to explain this to you, after we have already had a hashtag #MeToo movement, makes me feel uncomfortable.

So many have shared their #MeToo movement stories, and it was very empowering, but difficult to watch this movement of many taking back control of their lives, and their health.

Each person had a different story, but it didn't matter what that was because their story is valid and their feelings around it matter.

As I tell you this, my heartbeat is raising so fast that I don't even know if I can continue and I really want to delete this chapter. Or maybe just this section. It is so sad and only someone who has survived sexual interference at a young age would understand how this confuses a human who is a child that is learning from adults how to behave and what is normal in the world.

As an eight year old, it was so confusing to process and a really dark hole I entered because I was never able to talk about it with my parents, and when I did, they mostly displayed rage or dismissed the magnitude of what it meant for me. So I blocked it out for 10 years until one day somebody that I worked with at the age of 18 had dropped me off home after a work function. I said goodbye and I thought he had drove off or driven away, but whilst I was in the shower of my en suite bathroom in my Mermaid Beach home on the Gold Coast, he had somehow broken himself into my apartment (through the security door and into my front door) and entered my bedroom. When I walked out of the en suite shower, I was shocked and that evening changed my life.

It was that event of rape that had triggered a cascade of emotions that I had blocked out when I was eight years old.

For 10 whole years I didn't understand what had happened to me when I was eight. I hadn't even had a boyfriend yet so this was my "first time".

At the time of the eight year old incident, I had managed to eventually push the perpetrator out of my bedroom and with some struggle of two people, pushing the door both ways, I eventually shut that door, and managed to lock it. I must have fallen asleep in a heap, but when I woke up, the bedroom doors were off the hinges and off to the side.

I walked out and my father was quite full of rage. I now realize in hindsight why I blocked out communicating the incident. The perpetrator was also still around and was continuing to taunt me through the duration of the rest of the holiday when my family would tell me to go swim with him in the pool and I refused but he would insist and smirk.

Forgiveness in this moment is crucial for healing too. When you forgive others, you don't set them free, you set yourself free.

I don't like sharing this part of the book because I believe that some parts of our lives should be sacred.

There are so many things that go through my mind like "I'm holding back tears, and if I cry, I'll age me", but it's quite the contrary!

I know that releasing tears is therapeutic because tears have an analgesic effect. Tears that are sad hold analgesia.

Yet, I also worry about you and how this story makes you feel and how it may trigger you or just simply make you feel sad or mad.

Please know that if this has upset you or triggered you in anyway, I recommend that you seek professional help and support.

However, I decided that this story is so important to tell because it's the truth and it's my truth and it's the story of why I put in breast implants. It's also what I had to address to explant.

Being a wellness expert, if I didn't share this with you, you would never make sense of where this decision to augment came from.

On the other hand, I also have some kind of peace and understanding by sharing and documenting which is exactly what I want for you. I want you to create a way to safely release all your thoughts, emotions and narratives that have held you back from optimal health on every level.

Where my trauma to triumph really began was through this understanding and change of perception. It was only then that I was truly able to remove my implants and heal.

You see as a newly divorced woman in her early 40s I had decided to finally have the breast augmentation because in my head, I thought that putting something on me and on my chest was like a breast plate.

It was my my warrior woman's armor.

Isn't it profound that the implants that would sexualize me in an overt way, would remind me less of my prepubescent, traumatized child, and more of becoming a powerful sexualized new woman?

That was my psychology anyway. I didn't find it profound that it's on my chest and that underneath my Treasured Chest was my heart, exploding to be loved and protected.

Indeed, this decision and act of augmentation worked for a period of time. In fact, I forgot that they were there because I became a totally new person that no longer felt sad or disgusted by intimacy. Being in an intimate setting was always so confronting prior.

I was no longer triggered with my breast implants. But I was somebody else.

It was like this "protective armor" that put a barrier between me, the other person and my heart, was going to battle.

I did fall in love again, once or twice. But by this time I almost forgot that these breast were not all mine.

With an explant surgery now pending, I knew that I would have to remove my armor and face the act of intimacy alone without my protection. This was when I cried rivers! In other healing sessions with health professionals, I was in control of the timing and chosen the health professional but I did not choose the timing of the explant. It snuck up on me. Or did I choose it with divine timing and divinely guided?

I would begin my true healing journey now to really get ready to finally be free to be me!

I started reaching out to anyone and everyone I knew to find support, find en bloc or complete capsulectomy surgeons and prepare!

Before I tell you how my surgery actually went, let's reflect.

So, if we are to look back now, at all of the events that occurred, we could say that my first major trauma was probably when I was a baby, followed by a child sexual assault incident, at the age of eight, and then a rape a decade later, which transpired into an unhealthy relationship, and only when I divorced did I begin to really look at all the traumas. Was this a pattern? Indeed it was and I was determined to break the pattern!

The exact time of breast augmentation was at about the age of 42 and my son was about 3. That's when I augmented because I felt like it was important to finish the journey of breast rearing before I changed my body.

I called it breast rearing on purpose, because the feeding part is a very small part of the way in which our breasts raise our children.

It is comfort, it is nurture, immune cells, antibodies, analgesia, even teeth cleaning, in the way that the milk squirts out like a shower affect and babies store the milk in their cheeks and swallow at their own leisure. Breast-feeding or breast rearing is also great for speech development, and so many other health benefits, both physically and psychologically and spiritually.

I wrote my second book all about this, and it is called "The Modern Day Mother".

I really think that this is a very important and delicate subject to talk about because it is another precious time of a woman's life and also a very sensitive one. Not all women have breast-fed or were able to breast-feed.

My heart goes to all women and those who surrendered the bosom for all that it is to raise another human.

For those who never have the opportunity to mother, you have come from a mother, and we treasure her and her chest too. I treasure your chest because that's where your heart lays, and you are a wonderful nurturer, which is very maternal. In your heart of hearts, you already felt like a mother even though you are not one right now, I believe you are one to somebody else in this very moment.

I had finished breast-feeding of my son for a wonderful two years and 10 days and I counted those days because they were all so special especially because I never thought that I would get past even six months of feeding.

I was riddled with mastitis where the milk ducts are blocked and it is not only excruciating but very dangerous.

Mastitis can occur for a variety of reasons. It can be because of implants pressing on a milk duct. Some women have difficulty breast-feeding with implants in. Those women will never know until after the fact. Mastitis can also occur from too much pumping of your milk. It can interfere with the supply demand, which is so delicate, especially in the early stages of breast-feeding, where both mother and baby are learning and figuring out what is the best supply for them in this time. You will maybe have an over supply until you figure this out and pumping during this time can interrupt that delicate balance of creating the perfect amount that is designed, especially for the two of you or if you have twins, the three of you!

Mastitis can also occur when you are trying to time any feeds. Usually there is a supply there, because the baby is demanding it. If you are trying to train your baby and not feeding when the baby is demanding, it may also interfere with the milk ducts landing up being blocked.

Another reason for mastitis may be if you are wearing an underwire bra, or any kind of restrictive clothing that will block the milk ducts.

My mastitis occurred because I continued to listen to family members or others who care and wanted to help and who were telling me to time my feeds. They would tell me to not feed as often as I did.

I was 'feeding on demand' which is an attachment parenting style, but I don't like to label it as such. It was something that felt natural to me.

I soon learned through top lactation consultant and now dear friend; Pinky Mckay, who wrote the foreword to The Modern Day Mother, that 'feeding on demand" was not only normal and healthy, but also crucial because the supply is only there, because it is demanded by him and those demands are age-appropriate and that's why we supply.

We had to throw away the notion that it was just for calories or food. I realized that the feeding was so much more. This is why I am introducing the subject because it's another part of life where we really must treasure our chest.

It was a moment where I realized true connection, and absolute trust for another human that he was calling for me to breastfeed him for more reasons than just calories. It was for analgesia, for speech development, for nurture, for neurological development, and so many other things that we previously mentioned and it's selfless. It's an act that a man many never truly understand in the way we do. It's not like peeing. It's so much more.

So it was through that trust in breastfeeding on demand that I taught him trust too.

Even the W.H.O - the World Health Organization states that we should breastfeed until the age of two and beyond.

"Breastfeeding for the first six months is crucial development and health, and thereafter, to meet their evolving nutritional requirements, infants should receive nutritionally adequate and safe complementary foods, while continuing to be breastfed; and. breastfeeding should continue for up to two years or beyond." World Health Organization[1]

I can't believe I did the "beyond" part because I thought feeds would go forever but at the later ages, it was less frequent and more efficient.

When we started introducing solids, I soon learned that it was so much easier to feed breastmilk after introducing new foods, to help with his digestion. Most stop breast rearing once solids are being introduced but it takes a baby three weeks to develop the enzymes to digest a food after a new food is introduced. Feeding on the breast after a new food if he was asking for it, was a quick and efficient extraction and much easier to surrender to it than to be up all night with a baby that was sore, sick and needed medication.

Everybody's breastfeeding journey is unique though and different and it's an honor whether you did it for a long time or you decided not to or couldn't.

But this was my story and I cherish it because I was so lucky to have been supported by many health professionals and friends and as a result my son to this day, has never had any medication as a result of full term breastfeeding, his chiropractic care from birth and his healthy lifestyle.

When I had mastitis though, I wanted to stop breast feeding but instead I addressed the root cause of why it kept occurring. I realized I was trying to control the feeds and this in itself is another reoccurring pattern of where we as humans, try to control an outcome, it goes against us.

Instead of controlling, I learned the greatest life lesson, and that is to surrender to him, and his pure desire for breast rearing.

How we do anything is how we do everything and so this reflected in other areas of life that sometimes you can't swim against a tide and you just have to roll with this waves.

When I stopped timing and when I stopped controlling is when I was truly living.

For it is in those blissful moments that is what our sheer existence is about.

Can you draw analogy to other areas of your life where you may need to go with the flow a little more or surrender to an outcome?

Interestingly, my dedication to our breastfeeding journey didn't change the way I looked at all. In the beginning, obviously my breasts were bigger as they filled with milk, but because I hadn't stopped suddenly and allowed the milk to dry up slowly with mutual timing, we ended with a result that wasn't traumatic for either party.

Everyone has a different mutual time for them. We are all so unique and every family dynamic is different. We all do what's best for us.

Our mutual understanding was a dance between both seeing what's going to suit each other and that notion has not changed to this day, because I wanted to end it at two years, but he wanted a little bit longer, and between the two of us we negotiated until we eventually stopped at the two-year and 10 day mark.

This respectful negotiation still continues today with other things we do in life.

I believe that because it was a gentle way of stopping to breastfeed that my body went back to balance quite easily and naturally. My breasts still looked the way they did before I became pregnant, honestly, and I really didn't need to change my body at all for aesthetic reasons.

This is why I feel like it's triggering or a sensitive spot for any of us to communicate what our breasts have been through or what they look like. They tell a story.

Imagine when a surgeon tells you this story which is just a mere projection? "It won't look good anymore." Or "At your age, you're going to look saggy." Whether it's the truth, or whether it is a projection, why does it matter to us? Have they followed our lead in our pursuit for creating a younger looking aesthetic breast? Or have we groomed the surgeon and told them what we needed? I found myself educating my surgeon about what I believed was beautiful, and the more I went on this quest to find the right surgeon, the more I realized that a little bit of saggy was more than OK for me.

I think that they become concerned about giving us the outcome that they think we want, and at the end of the day we need to be at peace with what we are given whether we alter it or become at peace with the state of it naturally.

I also had an ex-lover or boyfriend that I think may have assisted in my decision to augment. He was into body building and there's a lot of augmentation in the body sculpting culture. He may have suggested I do it but I totally forgot about it until after the operation occurred and I went public. He must've seen it all on my social media and decided to reappear eight years later to apologize.

He sent me a very long message, explaining that he was a horrible human for how he treated me. It was both heartbreaking and healing to read.

I feel like we are all starting to wake up and realise the impact this is making.

Plastic surgeons' minds might be so conditioned that they sculpted us to be what they thought we wanted them to want us to be. It's all so interesting to observe and try and understand. I think we are all just figuring it out but we need to make peace and take change.

Before I became empowered and at peace with my decision on who to choose to explant, or on how it would land up looking, I was very confused, and all of this was a lot to process.

So many professional opinions stood in the way of me getting the explant right away.

Conflicting opinions and pricing are a lot to take on.

My explant surgeon and I had a conversation about how we couldn't understand some of the higher fees because it was like the doctors forgot about why they became a doctor in the first place - to help people and the Hippocratic oath they take which is to "Do no harm".

The Hippocratic Oath[2] is an oath of ethics historically taken by physicians. It is one of the most widely known of Greek medical texts. In its original form, it requires a new physician to swear, by a number of healing gods, to uphold specific ethical standards. The oath is the earliest expression of medical ethics in the Western world, establishing several principles of medical ethics which remain of paramount significance today. These include the principles of medical confidentiality and non-maleficence. As the seminal articulation of certain principles that continue to guide and inform medical practice, the ancient text is of more than historic and symbolic value. It is enshrined in the legal statutes of various jurisdictions, such that violations of the oath may carry criminal or other liability beyond the oath's symbolic nature.

The Greek physician Hippocrates (460–370 BC), to whom the oath is traditionally attributed

The original oath was written in Ionic Greek, between the fifth and third centuries BC[1] Although it is traditionally attributed to the Greek doctor Hippocrates and it is usually included in the Hippocratic Corpus, some modern scholars do not regard it as having been written by Hippocrates himself.

Hippocrates was the father of medicine. He always educated doctors to remind them that they had a teachers role and that they needed to educate their patients when it came to medicine. I often reflect on this, because I would also love a world where we didn't need the medical profession as much as we do.

How ready are you to become natural and normal?

Are you feeling resistance to undo the work that makes us sick?

How can something be adored or fondled whilst you're slowly dying inside?

I remember sitting in a restaurant / bar in Beverly Hills whilst I was waiting to be hopefully expedited with my February 20th appointment date. The man sitting next to me, was actually a cosmetic surgeon in the area and so we got talking. When I was explaining my pain to him, he looked at me with deep concern, and said "Where's 911?"

I wondered whether he was just being empathetic because during this time my case had not been described as an emergency yet.

Let me tell you about how I took charge during the day before and morning of my operation. The lead up to my surgery and what my waiting room experience was like.

There are rules in life but there's also exceptions to every rule and a patient's needs to feel safe are paramount.

On the morning of my surgery, I was dropped off by my dear friend Rosa. When I checked in at the front desk, I was asked to sit in the waiting room and the nurse would collect me. This waiting room didn't feel great. It felt like negative and clinical energy.

It was a private hospital so some would say it's better than a public system but all the chairs were facing the front desk and big television screens were facing all the chairs showing the news.

I didn't want to have to watch bad news and more drama. I needed to go into this operation and manifest my own special outcome.

The lead up to my surgery was already made special with my dear friends, Rosa and Dylan who had arranged a surprise dinner party for me with my son at her house the night before. I came back from the beach and I was greeted at the door with a surprise on the balcony.

Rosa said she wanted to distract me. She wanted me to have something to do the night before I was about to remove my implants. She consciously created a party to celebrate the beginning of my brand new life and we celebrated it!

I started to get excited about it all and visualized how well the surgery would go and how I'd feel well instantly.

I was imagining that I'd wake from a deep sleep or dream and be this person I've always wanted to be.

I had bad reactions to anesthetic in my previous surgery with the augmentation. I woke feeling nauseas and had urine retention which was frightening. So I needed to make sure I was relaxed and got to speak to the anesthesiologist prior.

The food spread was healthy and this was my time to make that manifestation happen. In the moments leading up to being taken into the surgery room, all these moments are paramount.

Only when you're about to die, do you truly know how to live.

Are you consciously living and designing your best life?

Then Doctor Gordon, the anesthesiologist, rang to ask me about my previous reactions. I gave him my history and he told me he had just the right way to look after me. He said he would micro dose. I felt at ease now and thanked him for calling and told him he had a nice voice. He told me I had a nice voice too.

I then asked him if I could have a glass of red wine with my friends before I fasted, to relax. He said that sounded lovely and gave me approval.

When I went to tell Rosa and Dylan what happened, they joked and said, "Next minute the door bell rings and Doctor Gordon is here with wine!" It made me realise that there was a human element that felt so nice and I said that I couldn't wait to meet him.

My friends asked me what I thought Dr. Gordon would look like. I'm quite psychic and replied that I'm visualizing him to have light skin and perhaps freckles with brown hair or even a ginger tone.

We all had a game of guessing what Dr. Gordon looks like and everybody said something different. It was a fun evening and those moments helped me to carry that energy through into the waiting room.

This is why I refused to sit and stare at the negative news on the television screens. I looked behind me and I saw a prayer room that wasn't being used.

I've never been spiritual or religious, but I've always believed in a greater force than us that looks after us, because we are connected to it.

So I decided to go into the prayer room and do whatever I needed to do to make myself feel calm going into the operation. My body was about to be asleep for a long time and I wanted it to have some movement and beautiful shorts before it was about to go under anesthetic.

There was a Bible in the room, but I pushed it to the side and started doing some yoga stretches. I then put some gentle, relaxation music on my phone. Releasing tension with gentle movement was fantastic but the music starting to make me cry. I think I was purging the old me and releasing, but I guess a little part of me was naturally scared too. I decided to put on some happy music and played Fleetwood Mac!

This music made me start dancing and drumming on the Ottoman chair. It really lifted my spirits, and then I was collected to go and see the nurse. Normally we would have our phones taken away from us at this point, but I had told her that I had a history of PTSD and that this music was really helping me to feel calm and happy. She asked her colleagues and they confirmed it would be OK for a little bit longer. When I got taken in to finally see the anesthetist, that's when my phone was no longer permitted, but they did suggest that they could gently put on the music on the computer screen in the background.

I thought it was such an interesting moment that I was orchestrating the perfect surgery for me. Sometimes when you have needs and they are communicated reasonably, why wouldn't we be able to have those needs met?

I started to get excited and then Dr. Gordon walked in. He looked exactly how I visualized. The confirmation was an affirmation that my intuition is always right.

He quipped, "Nice choice of music!" I was glad he enjoyed it too and then we got started with the preparation for the anesthesia. He asked. "Any other requests?" I said, "Some reiki perhaps?" I was half joking but not really since he asked. We laughed. Laughter is good. I asked him if he could say nice things to me as I'm going under. He replied, "I'll be saying nice things to you the whole time." There's the power of intention and language.

I was obviously a little bit nervous still and so he was in tune with making sure I was comfortable. A very professional doctor with a beautiful bedside manner. He then asked me if I was ready to be wheeled in. My mind instantly went to when I birthed my son naturally. My midwife at the time was getting me ready to go to the birthing center as I was having the first stages of contraction. I wanted to go in my dressing gown. Jan Ireland said to me, "You're not sick! Put on your favourite outfit! We are having a birth day!" That life experience taught me that going into a hospital doesn't have to be about sickness and disease and suffering. I then I used this reflection to dictate my next actions.

I told Dr. Gordon that I thought we should walk in together. He agreed and said "What a fabulous idea!". He said that he thought there was nothing more empowering than a patient walking themselves in. I explained that patients suffer and I wasn't in his care to continue suffering. I was there to be well. So with that, we got up and started walking in and all I could see was a very stark white, bright clinical room, which looked brighter than anything I have ever seen in my life.

It was like I had walked into heaven and the lights were taking me to another place.

The nurse is rushed up to him and said, "What are you doing?" he told him it was OK. He said, "We are walking in and I'm holding the back of her gown for dignity." Honestly, I didn't even realize, but what I didn't know was that I felt like I was completely in control. I finally turned a very traumatic event into triumphant one.

And of course everything that I wished for came true when I woke. I didn't feel any nausea and I felt nothing but fantastic and rebirthed. It was incredible that even with the uncomfortability of the scars from the surgery and the trauma that my body felt after having removed something so big, that I still felt instantly elated and more well. A lot of others expressed similar. They have often shared with me that as soon as they woke, they felt like a huge weight was lifted off their chest, literally!

My surgeon at Sydney Macquarie University, Professor Anand Deva, exclaimed, "Wow, you were right! There was a rupture in the implant on the left side exactly where you pinpoint telling me. You're better than an MRI! You really taught me something today! I'm going to go back and check all my patients."

I guess my body really was shutting down and caving in. I guess I knew all this time. Just like when you listen to your heart, because what it is telling you will never go away, we need to also listen to our bodies, signs and signals. The symptom is always the sign and we'll always give you what you need to know.

A lot of people talk about staring death in the face and having 'spiritual awakenings'.

I definitely had my big spiritual awakening. I guess I didn't die. But the implant bags tried to kill me.

I feel like this book is my memoir of a major great awakening on my spirituality since all the dots just started to connect.

I know that this may create the same effect for you, that you may ponder on where are you felt like you had a spiritual, awakening, or where you need to listen to your body more.

Just hours after my explant February 20, 2023 with my son, Beaudy.

Maybe there was a trauma that you perceived in your life, but upon reflection, and reading these paragraphs, you realize that you can turn them into a triumphant face and lots of experience.

If you are reading this and have an upcoming surgery, or something big in your life, then know that some of this information will rub off and help you to change your perception about what's happening to you and for you in your life. You have the power to make the changes and create an outcome that is more positive.

I want this empowerment for you without you having to go through the trauma. Like most parents that care for their kids, or anyone who cares about anyone, we hate to see people suffering. We try to desperately protect them from it. However, sometimes the greatest growth comes from the greatest pain.

Or maybe you will have an end or closure to so part of your life that needed to be faced.

You will you really reflect on the information in this chapter and allow it to transform you instead of 'try' you.

And this is the divine message. We need each other! This is because we are each other. We are the same. We are connected. This is a spiritual awakening message that circles back to all of the health messages I have ever written about which explores exactly how we are innately designed to self heal and adapt when we are given the right environment.

That environment is to be as close to nature as possible. It's to eat as close to nature as possible. This is living naturally, and in this notion, what is natural is to be together and to help one another. Not only are we connected through the universe which facilitates our innate intelligence ability to heal, but we are also connected in community, and this is crucial for health and wellness.

Somehow, in the western world, we choose to live so far away from each other in big houses that we forget to tell one another that we don't really have it all going on, on our own.

Just like it takes a village to raise a child, it also takes a community to keep us well. The more we share our trauma or pain or trials and tribulations, the more we can relate, and we rise by lifting others.

What have you failed to acknowledge? What have you been too shy to share?

What, if bravely sharing these things were the very thing that could help you to be well and ultimately the most empowered version of you? What if the people that you are meant to meet present as a result?

I know that they will present because the minute I accepted this as my journey, and became as bravely honest as I could, even though I wanted to vomit at times I purged out my truth, the right people gathered. You reading this book is an example of the right people. I hope this is starting to make sense for you.

From how I flipped the experience of the waiting room protocol prior to my explant surgery and how I spun the terrible story to change perception so that I come out the stronger one, or how I choose to change any narrative that serves me more, is what I want to teach you.

This lesson also came from a Media Lawyer that kindly worked for me several years ago on a pro bono basis, because he saw that I was suffering with PTSD as a result of not a traumatic event as such, but how media dragged me into an event that became traumatic. It made me feel very unsafe and scared and attached to a story that had nothing to do with me.

I saw the media organization had included my image but had doctored it. The media outlet did not realise this was defamation as not with words but rather with imagery. My lawyer wrote a letter in my defense to take action and demanded a retraction of this photograph, as well as a public apology. If we continued litigation, maybe I would've received this and more, but we realized that just by the media company retracting the photograph that was altered, was them showing us that they actually (by default) admitted that it was defamation.

I didn't get a public apology and I wasn't compensated, but he did share with me that the justice system isn't always just and that it can also be exhausting. This story is paramount because what he taught me was that you can seek justice in other ways. He told me that I am a brilliant storyteller and broadcaster, and that one day I can share my story which will help me to seek justice in my own way. The story will probably be the next book. What are your gifts though? Who's helping you see them?

Meanwhile, use this excellent suggestion to prevent mud from sticking.

"Life won't always go the way you want it to. What you do have control over though is how you react to it".

I continue to make conscious choices on what feels better and healthier for me so that I can empower you. This is the part I want you to treasure and hold close to your chest forever.

Remember that you've got you.

I knew that the release of my holistic health guide, Connected, was special and came at a very prominent time. The health guide aims to heal the divide between allopathy and wellness by empowering the reader to understand we need both, (at different times). So as angry as we are, that are many class actions brewing with breast implant illness sufferers. Many manufacturers are becoming solvent so we still need the surgeons to help us. We need to find a way to educate them and all work together.

It's this running theme that we must all always work together. Sure we can blame surgeons but we will still always need them. It is my wish in my belief that there are many good surgeons who are educating the others in their peer groups and their conferences and their seminars on what is really going on and how they can better serve us.

The sad reality is that as I type, we still don't have enough trained explanting surgeons to remove implants when we need them. You won't always be triaged and most likely will be put on a wait list.

It's only through education to the patient and the industry understanding us, that we can all find a way to work together that's in the best interest of the patient because never has there been a more prominent time where the sufferer is the expert.

Right now we are educating surgeons on what breast implant illness even is. They're still learning from us with study groups like the one I'm in with NSW Health or from the countless women taking to social media.

Or like my case where you discovered that it was only after I was operated on, that indeed I really had an emergency. I had an undetected rupture exactly where I was pinpointing to for many years. That's an emergency, right?

We are all still learning and prevention is always the cure.

Making peace with my trauma in this journey as I suffered led me to question if this was a life path that was already mapped out for me?

Of course it's something I wish could've been avoided. My health has not been the same since. I've had to work extremely hard on avoiding a myriad of illnesses from setting in. My hair loss is indicating that something deeper is going on and I'm still having blood work done and my other CFS (chronic fatigue syndrome) like symptoms that have developed are all markers that I need to get to the bottom of it.

In making peace with this path though, I reflect on my life long commitment to wellness education.

I recall the day I shot the cover of Connected, a paradigm shift in how we view health. It was shot on the 11th and at 4:11 PM on the eve of when we had a new curfew set in, in Melbourne, Australia (the most locked down city in the world). It was a part of the new rules and regulations around the pandemic when the virus became more contagious from 6pm onwards.

That's when the curfew began - 6 PM!

So, that day it was announced, I knew I needed to shoot the cover with the golden light before we weren't allowed to even step outside ever again.

It was a real race to the finish line to be outside and I felt weirdly nervous shooting an image for the cover of my book, having to take full advantage of that day.

I remember being with my photographer in a remote area, by the ocean with hardly anyone in sight, on the beach, dancing on a rock, in the water, barefoot in an $8000 couture Jason Grech dress.

My son was holding the light reflector. We weren't allowed to work unless it was a job in "essential services". We could go out for an hour a day to walk and get movement with the people in your home. I was with those people and dancing and moving. It felt surreal and I was committed to the outcome.

It was a day I felt in true service.

So many angel numbers have appeared since then coincidentally, although nothing is a coincidence!

Even media launches happened in November, which was the 11th month and times of 11 AM, or 1pm, but I didn't realize until after the invitations were sent.

Sometimes you may notice coincidences like this and feel like you are completely on path. Please don't let them go unnoticed.

For me, it's been numbers but for you it may be a song, a rainbow that consistently appears, a spirit animal or recurrent dream or any other feeling that makes you feel like you're on a path.

I want you to draw on those feelings of a memory when you felt like you were having a déjà vu moment because in that moment is where absolute magic is happening even when you feel like things are going wrong, they are actually going right.

This is the part you'll learn that helps you feel like you're going to be ok if you can transcend obstacles into transformation.

Keeping this in mind, you'll start to see that your life is already all mapped out for you and making peace with that path is where you can start to put more energy into creation instead of getting too dwelled on why things aren't going a certain way.

We are here to create and procreate and as creative beings, we can totally manifest the most magical world and health, but you must really be aware of the game of life and I call it a test.

You will constantly be tried and tested in life to continue to ask yourself the question of "Is this where I want to be?" If not, change it!

It doesn't mean you'll let perpetrators take advantage or allow anyone to take advantage. It means you'll calmly go about seeking truth, your own definition of Justice and a feeling of peace by taking control of your entire life and the way you want the outcome to go.

If you feel like something is holding you back from your most ideal 'well world' then you have the capacity to find the people, resources, support, and places to change that.

In the back of this book is a whole chapter of resources to help you. Additionally, I just love helping you evolve through my wellness coaching, podcasts and other books.

Or if your empowered path doesn't exist right now, you are a creator and you can create it!

I never thought this was truly possible to the extent I've recently learned and only now that I live in an entirely new continent with my son and raising him successfully alone, (after I almost died) do I now know that everything is possible.

I did find myself in a world where it hasn't been ideal. In fact, it has been quite traumatic at times and sometimes I wondered why I had to endure so much trauma. I no longer question it because turning my darkness into light for others has become somewhat of a gift I'm now sharing. We need to move past the pain to truly heal.

Little do you know, (until now, as you are about to read the following chapters) that everything I have done with such light and love and beautiful energy is as a result of the hardship in my life that I wanted so much to 'gift you' with and light you up. My three decades of teaching health and wellness is a commitment in service to educating humanity to live a better quality of life naturally.

Even when things weren't easy or peaceful for me, I created my own community and created educated readers that can continue to share the knowledge I have empowered them with.

For some of you this is the 10th book that you have read of mine. Whether this is the first book or the 10th one, I am so grateful and feel privileged for the opportunity to share with you. Something that is going to be very intimate, extremely insightful and inspiring.

This is exactly why I write! I want to empower you. I can only do that when I continue to empower myself, for we are all mirrors and reflections of each other. The beauty you see in me is the beauty you see in you. The light you see in me is the light you see in you. If you were to give me a compliment, I am highly aware of the compliment you are giving yourself.

If you are to 'trash talk' me, I am highly aware that it is a projection, or rather your 'inner voice' to yourself. Your negative comments are only as a result of somebody speaking like that to you, or your unhealed trauma cause you're in a narrative now.

The less 'evolved me', would have taken it very personally, as I'm a sensitive Cancerian astrology sign.

However now, as I continue to evolve and do the deep work on myself, all I do is continue to love you harder so that I can reflect that love and you can become more of that.

We no longer want division because through our podcasts and stories and events and shows or songs we can find similarities instead of indifference.

If you cannot reflect the love that I share with you, it's just your soul's journey and that's OK. We all have our own path. Maybe in your next lifetime?

This hasn't been an easy book to write. This is largely, because I am still healing from a series of physical and emotional trauma or events, but I am aware that in our constant feed to process and grow.

However, the more I write, the more cathartic and free I feel.

Pain shouldn't stop us from sharing, engaging, and contributing to the world. So many times we wait until something is perfect, but what if it is all perfect right now as we are in this imperfect state?

This very notion is actually an analogy for the entire content of this book. You see we have been living in a world and culture of creating normalization of breast, implants and other modifications to our perfect human body. It is within this observation, and witnessing that,

I have discovered humanity continues to choose to only be happy when things are perfect. And guess what? They never are, because they already are, if you know what I mean?

It is through the process of shedding or removing breast implants and rediscovering true beauty of your inner self that so many finally heal and transform into everything they always wanted to be.

Isn't that ironic? This is a gift from us, that can sometimes bring ourselves back to our truth and turn it all into triumph.

I was doing the same in the sauna and did a social media post about it! My implant with an undetected rupture was melting in me and also exploding upon return on my flight back to Australia to explant on the descend, due to the pressure!

I couldn't make a complaint to the FDA or the manufacturer. My implants were by a company called Silimed. The company had disappeared. Gone. Ordered to close.

I didn't know. I only discovered this when my explant surgeon told me the company was urged to shut shop in 2016.

Why wasn't I informed?

I remember sending a direct message on Instagram when I first landed in America to an Aussie friend living in Los Angeles. I was telling him how sick I am and he shared he had many friends who had their implants removed and felt so much better but I couldn't afford the operation! That was half the stress.

He explained that there's now a loan that women could take out especially for the explant surgery. That's in America. In Australia, if you have any superannuation saved, you're allowed to ask the Australian Taxation office to let them release it to you on compassionate grounds for a life-threatening illness operation.

My heart goes out to all women reading this now and feeling the same. You know you're dying slowly and you have to stay well to earn so you can get well.

A health coach who was working for a renowned plastic surgery in Beverly Hills was helping me to set up an appointment with the surgeon that she worked for. I was hoping that his fees would be less than US$14,000. I had paid another US$400 to him to secure my initial consultation, but just days before my appointment with him, she called me to tell me that there would be no way that he would discount my visit. She told me to "manifest the money".

It's unfortunate that I was in a financial predicament and unable to afford the operation that I needed but this realization only came in hindsight. The sad reality is that these surgeons are in private practice and can do whatever they want with their practices and their fees. So many of us don't plan for this day that eventually comes and this is why I felt compelled to expose what's going on for us all.

I was in America and didn't have an opportunity to apply for the loan so in the end I had to access my superannuation. Among other reasons, one of the reasons why I flew back to Australia was to choose Professor Anand Deva as my surgeon.

We always have to look on the bright side and know that eventually we will find a way to improve our system. Maybe this book is doing just that?

It's been only a matter of months and let's take a look at what has improved so far for me post operation:

Prior to the removal of my breast implants and their surrounding tissue, I suffered:

◊ Brain fog and confusion

◊ Tinnitus and brain buzzing like I'm an antenna (heavy metals bouncing around interacting with 5G radiation)

◊ Localized pain in the left breast where the undetected rupture was. I had a pressing on the rib cage from week one which I reported but it got progressively worse year after year. I was told it was just a fold.

◊ Food intolerances

◊ Mast cell activation syndrome

◊ Stage two contracture, and the implant sliding into and in between my rib cage with the ribs and clavicle and shoulder, slowly dislocating and going out of alignment.

◊ Feelings of suicide or felt like I was dying because my system is shutting down

◊ Loss of libido

◊ Inability to breathe deeply

◊ Sleeplessness and night sweats

◊ Anxiety and depression and medical gaslighting telling me that nothing was urgent and questioning whether it really was implant illness or something else

◊ Inflammation

◊ Continual hair loss

◊ Bowel and digestive disorders like SIBO / constipation - passing stools once every five days and prior to surgery I had not eliminated any waste for 10 days!

◊ Not sweating for about one year!

◊ Insatiable thirst
◊ Heart palpitations
◊ Internal anal bleeding

NEW ME: Six weeks later post explant and post complete capsulectomy surgery:

Instantly I had…

◊ Clarity of thought and memory improving
◊ Instantly no longer wanted to die or feelings of death
◊ Much more energy and better sleep
◊ Regular bowel movements
◊ Ability to sweat
◊ Ability to assimilate nutrition and less constant thirst
◊ No depression but anxiety still present with concerns of spillage of the silicone
◊ Pain in the left breast but potentially from scar tissue and surgery.
◊ Instant libido returning
◊ No longer as intolerant to gluten and observing other foods
◊ Observation of hair loss and potential slowing down of baldness
◊ Small / cute breasts
◊ Feelings of empowerment, unstoppable and unfuckwithable / survivor mentality with added wisdom

Three months post surgery I had:

◊ Mast cell activation syndrome flare ups
◊ Pectoral damage
◊ Hair loss worsened
◊ SIBO returned

◊ Mental health improved immensely

◊ Breasts looking a little softer and less full but made peace with my natural state

◊ Full upper body movement and strength returning

◊ Less anxiety

◊ Ability to breathe deeply again

◊ Left breast pain gone but observed a little lump where the rupture and fold was to keep an eye on

◊ Seldom headaches and sweats

Four and a half months post surgery;

◊ I am on a beach and writing this book as often as I can. I'm committed to staying connected to nature and taking this healing journey slowly. I've had blood tests that were ordered by my integrative medical doctor, which you will soon hear from in the following chapter. We are currently looking closely at the possibility of autoimmune disease that can sometimes occur as a result of a silicon implant lake that then causes alopecia in women.

A case-control study that included 40 AA patients and 40 apparently healthy matched controls. Written informed consents were obtained from all the participants. The scalp was examined to assess sites, number, and size of alopecia patches, and the severity of AA lesions was assessed using the Severity of Alopecia Tool score (SALT score) which determine the percentage of hair loss in the scalp. The body was carefully examined to detect any alopecia patches in any hairy area. Nail examination was carried out to detect any nail involvement. Serum IL-15 levels were measured using an ELISA kits.

Results: Serum levels of IL-15 in patients were significantly higher than those in the control group ($P < 0.001$). Serum levels in alopecia totalis were significantly higher than those with one or two patches, and serum levels in patients with both scalp and body involvement were significantly elevated than the levels of patients with either scalp or body involvement. There was a statistically significant positive correlation between SALT score and serum levels of IL-15 (P < 0.001).

Conclusion: Serum IL-15 may be a marker of AA severity[8].

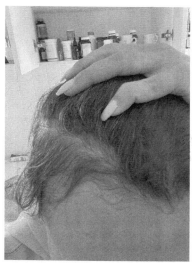

So after we remove our implants, the journey is still a long one. Of course, a lot of things can improve instantly but we need to stay on top of it all. It's important to continue working with your medical practitioner, integrative medical doctor and your natural healthcare practitioner of choice like a naturopath, chiropractor or kinesiologist.

What are your symptoms? Do you know anyone with implants that has the symptoms?

This next part is so difficult to share with you, partly because I carry shame that it was me, but I realise this story was a part of me that wasn't well and I'm so glad I can look at it in hindsight and tell you definitively that this story was because I knew I was dying and shutting down but nobody believed me.

So here it goes! My son reminded me when we returned from Australia after I had the surgery, and we got home to Beverly Hills, that I was in our home on the rug he was pointing to, and reminded me what I said and did.

He reminded me that I was on the carpet rug and I kept telling him I was dying or that I had cancer and wanted to die. In hindsight, I guess that were true. I just couldn't describe what it was.

Even though I knew the power of thought and these positive beliefs, wellness practices and chiropractic were keeping me stable, that's all they were doing and usually I'd be thriving but instead I was merely surviving.

It's crazy that I forgot about it as soon as my implants were removed out of me and my body could get back to healing and thriving safely. It's like I was done with those thoughts and truths and immediately onto a new one that I knew I was creating. I didn't need to think those thoughts anymore because I wasn't actually crazy or going crazy. I was merely shutting down systemically one organ at a time and now I'm not.

He had to reenact the moment on the daybed though to trigger my memory about it and then coupled it with his reassuring notion that he knew I didn't mean it but just wanted to be operated on.

That was reassuring that he already has the wisdom to know this and that in hindsight he was also someone who was keeping me mentally stable so that we could stay healthy enough to have my operation on that awaited date of 20 February 2023.

So many others feel the same. There's just not enough spots to operate or the system won't believe how sick you really are so they dismiss you.

I think it shows how very strong we are that we carry on, show up, dress up and wear make up to hide what's really going on and carry on with our lives.

The ability to learn new things was a really difficult one to describe to others who weren't suffering similar. I was literally on the phone to people saying I can't understand, that I can't do it and I thought that I was mentally unwell but I was just systemically ill. If we create more awareness around what this is, then others will have more patience for us, whilst we await our surgery date.

I am about to enlighten you with what you need to do to prepare for the surgery. It's very important that you choose the right surgeon for you, create a financial way to do so, create a support system with your community friends and loved ones, and you must also arm your self with anything you feel you need to do from a legal standpoint.

Would you trust a surgeon that removes implants but still augments? Have a think about that one also?

Do you know what's even crazier? My own diagnosing doctor wasn't able to keep the implants she paid for. They wouldn't give them to her. Luckily, through her misfortune, which is really bittersweet, she was able to educate me and warned me by preparing them to ask for them. It's not always standard practice to give you your implants back after the surgery. That's your evidence that they were in you. Should you ever choose to join a class action, they'll be necessary. Nonetheless, the most important thing is to also send the surrounding scar tissue and catchers to the labs to be tested for various things, like mold, bacteria, various cancers and carcinoma.

Luckily, mine came back clear. However, we still don't know the long-term ramifications of the silicone leakage and spillage.

Here is your checklist for preparation for a better surgery outcome:

- ◊ Keep yourself stable with quality nutrition prescribed from your integrative medical doctor or naturopathic doctor.

- ◊ Keep your body in alignment and your nervous system free of interference with chiropractic care

◊ Keep an eye on your symptoms and record them regularly. Ask for regular check ups with your implanting surgeon and the surgeon that you chose to explant with.

◊ Upon choosing your explant surgeon, you may decide to go by recommendations from others that have said that they were happy with their outcome.

◊ Take into consideration if you will need to stay and recover for a period of time and if you will need somebody to look after you. If you choose to have the operation away from your family and loved ones then you may need to hire someone to care for you for a week.

◊ Make sure that you are financially in a position to pay for not just the operation but the hospital fees, anesthetist and any medication that may follow or treatment that   may follow.

◊ You may be able to get a loan from a bank or you may also be eligible for an early release of your Australian taxation office approved superannuation that is given to you on compassionate grounds for a life-threatening illness operation.

◊ Be prepared with healing foods post operation. we will discuss more about this in the following chapter with a detox protocol.

◊ Make sure that you have comfortable bedding and cushions that you are able to sleep well post operation as you may need to sleep upright for the first couple of nights.

◊ Make sure that your surgeon is aware that you want to keep your implants. You must put in writing in an email that not only would you like to have your implants given back to you but you would like it to be photographed, videoed and recorded with the serial numbers shown and sealed up for you to take home. Make sure that your surrounding scar tissue is going to be sent off for testing.

How to go about withdrawing your superannuation on compassionate grounds for a life-threatening illness operation:

1. Book in with your general practitioner medical doctor in Australia. Have them write a referral for your chosen surgeon who is a specialist in complete capsulectomy.

2. Your surgeon will fill out a form for you to present to the Australian Taxation Office (ATO) The Australian Taxation Office will then need to review your submission along with your financial information and letter from both your referring doctor and surgeon. If they can see that you are indeed under financial hardship, they will then issue an acceptance and you will receive a copy of this letter. They will also send a letter to your superannuation fund.

3. Once your superannuation fund has received the letter from the Australian Taxation Office, you are then able to fill out a form which allows you to release your superannuation on compassionate grounds for a life-threatening illness operation. With both of these forms, your superannuation fund will then release your superannuation of the exact amount that is required to have the operation and it should take about three weeks in total.

The long-term studies on breast implant illness have not really been reported yet. That's why research work from Professor Anand Deva and the like in the medical profession are very important people to support. Even though he knows the very real risks and deadly ramifications that implants cause, he said to me in my consult because of the work that I was doing in the media, that was so effective and something that would impact others . He knew that of course once women knew more, that they would be very upset.

There aren't enough surgeons that are charging reasonable fees and able to perform the explant surgery on the women once they join dots.

With all the media I was doing, to hear from women like me who are bold and brave enough to explain with emphatic certainty and conviction that your symptoms are real, we need data in this crazy world to support it is absurd. Also, just be careful that these women have not had other illnesses prior to them having implants. It may have gone unnoticed or under diagnosed. The reality though, is that because an implant is an inflammatory driver, whether there was a pre-existing illness, or it has created an early onset of a genetic predisposed illness or created a brand new one, all of these things still respond very well to not having an implant in a human body.

"You did this to yourself".

I keep exploring this as one of the western world narratives.

My story represents the fragility of a person and their narrative they carry. It helps the reader (all of you) who are to understand that each human has their own soul's journey, and why they do anything so that we can feel less judgment towards the person, but rather their story they carry and the system we live in.

It's no doubt that feeling like there is no rush, or there is no guarantee for a certain outcome, for we are all still learning as we go, I can feel quite unsafe, but this really is a case of at some point, us all understanding that it doesn't matter which company manufacturer, textured, or smooth, round, or teardrop, saline, or silicone, that there always seems to be some kind of complication, and in my opinion, that no implant is ever really safe. Just coming to this conclusion and realizing not just me but many others don't want implants anymore, is a triumphant fete in history.

Let's keep you feeling empowered in all the way you want, and let's hear from the doctors that want this for us in the next chapter. It's time for some eye-opening statistics and cold hard facts.

Chapter 5

Stats and Facts

Contributors -

Dr Tania Ash & Professor Anand Deva

"All truth passes through three stages. First, it is ridiculed. Second, it is violently opposed. Third, it is accepted as being self-evident."

Arthur Schopenhauer, Philosopher

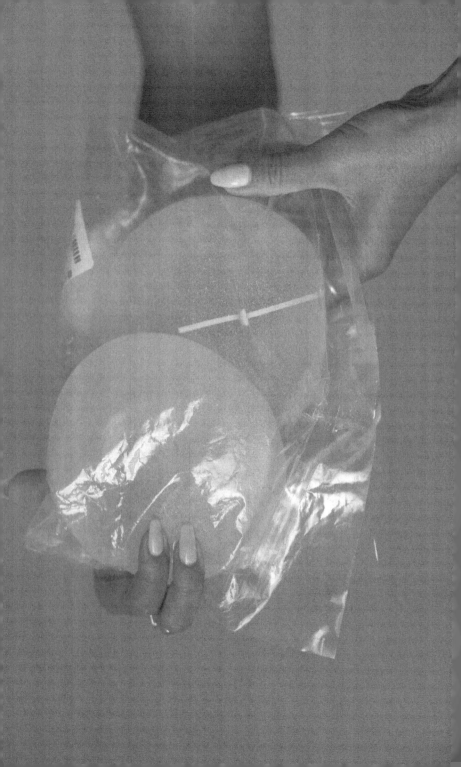

I have been researching health and wellness for 30 years, this 'new' subject is actually not that new.

I see myself in this health title I called "Treasured Chest" as more of an investigative reporter role, narrator and researcher. I'm usually known as a wellness expert but I would like to say that everything you have read so far is more of a memoir as well as someone who's privy to extensive information from other health professionals such as the two you're about to hear from as contributors for this book.

They were also my diagnosing doctor, Dr Tania Ash and my explant surgeon, Professor Anand Deva.

Together, we worked to make sure I got well and now we are committed to helping you and many others. This is why I love working with great doctors. They understand that the word "doctor", means "teacher" and that this Latin meaning means that we are needing to educate!

Just like the Thomas Edison quote, who was the man who invented the lightbulb, said *"The doctor of the future will give no medicine, but will interest his patient in the care of the human frame, in diet and in the cause and prevention of disease"*.

What's needed of you to serve your community too and help others? This book is the catalyst for something that will begin a cascade of women and all people who have implants holding space for each other. It will create a snowball effect of health professionals supporting us the way we need to. It will allow us access to funds to be able to afford it better.

Facebook groups and others will also create support that I didn't even know could happen or that we may need. That's the beauty of life's surprises. I know that this movement will inspire millions to create their own platforms and to help us all feel supported, loved, heard and held.

At the end of the day, we must remove all doubt about the questions we have previously had that make us emphatically feel that we are going crazy and that we don't have an implant illness. It's more often than not that we do.

Before you undergo any surgery, and in particular this one, it is crucial to research on every level and of course investigate what's going on for you in your own body to make sure that you are well and safe.

Don't you worry, I had so much doubt and questioned whether I really had breast implant illness, I would ask myself;

"What if it is something else? What if I can address that? Perhaps I really am just getting older or it is PTSD or perhaps it's just a food intolerance?"

Indeed, most health challenges are multifactorial, and it is important for us to look at all of our history and symptoms that present. Just know that no matter what your genetic predisposition is or what other illnesses were going on prior to your implants, as well as the current new symptoms, the point is that your body is going to be better off without this inflammatory driver of your implants.

At some point we start to join the dots and realize that because any health challenge can be a myriad of other things that are contributing, it's always multifactorial, no matter what and having implants is an accumulation affect.

Additionally, there was a support group that included one gentleman. I remember him saying underneath one of the posts that he was so excited he found his tribe! This gentleman had calf muscle implants. He said that he had the exact same symptoms as all the women.

At some point we start to learn that the body cannot adapt any longer to these inflammatory drivers and your genetic predispositions may start to become expressed as a result of the extra burden or stress or in the body.

So the question is - why not give my body an optimal chance to be able to heal and express health better? Why do I want to fast track any kind of genetic predisposition illness from occurring?

In case you missed it, cosmetic surgery is not all it 'busts out' to be!

Even though this phase of my life initially somewhat helped my mental wellness, (although it was a 'patch up' solution) at what cost do you risk your overall health?

The 'patch up' solution like any drugs or medicine may be good to save you from what you're experiencing but at some point, you'll need to go back and address the root issues or clean up the mess.

I'm not the only one starting to realise. Millions over the world are desperate to have their symptoms from the systemic response and inflammatory storm that implants cause, validated.

Breast implant illness you'll soon learn, is actually "mast cell activation syndrome"and it's real. The mast cells (immune cells) start to attack one another and your entire body often shuts down (like mine was) once you start to reject the implants.

Dr Tania Ash, who assisted me on my journey back to health, is still a huge part of my life. She is always contributing to the medical profession with her knowledge about what breast implant illness really is and her area of expertise is this and what she believes is actually MCAS - mast cell activation syndrome. What a bittersweet pill that Dr. Tania had to endure this horrible disease so that she could help others. She knows firsthand how this feels and how it can be helped.

We all pay for it in more ways than one and it's costly. Let's not forget there's not enough specialist surgeons that can remove the scar tissue capsule with the bag, so leaving that inside is potentially leaving the carcinoma in.

I only just survived an undetected rupture that six surgeons over two years (or more) didn't detect.

I was slowing dying with all bodily symptoms shutting down. I wanted my implants removed when everyone said there was no leak. I insisted and kept asking to be triaged. Finally on 20 February 2023, I returned to Sydney and had a ground breaking surgery where the scar tissue was removed with the bag.

I'm redefining beauty standards, whilst empowering women all over the world to get ready to remove.

You don't need an undetected rupture like me to suffer implant illness. There's mold, bacteria, new types of capsule cancers and leaks in valves.

The AMA (American Medical Association) journal has reported:

The first major silicone breast implant lawsuit was in 1984, when Maria Stern won $211,000 in compensatory damages and $1.5 million in punitive damages from silicone breast implant manufacturer Dow Corning after claiming that her breast implants caused autoimmune disease. At the trial, Stern introduced as evidence Dow Corning internal documents suggesting that the company was aware of high rupture rates and gel bleed with silicone breast implants.

The Stern lawsuit went largely unnoticed until 1990 when, on the eve of congressional hearings on the safety of breast implants, a program on the dangers of silicone implants aired on Face to Face with Connie Chung.

Interestingly, the only three scientific experts who testified at the subsequent congressional hearings were also paid expert witnesses for plaintiffs in breast implant litigation. Pressured by congressional hearings and media reports, the FDA's General and Plastic Surgery Devices Panel met to discuss the safety of silicone breast implants. Medical organizations, including the American Medical Association, urged the panel to oppose a ban on implants. The panel agreed that silicone breast implant manufacturers had submitted safety data insufficient to resolve the issue and recommended that the implants remain available pending further safety studies[3].

Decades later, we still have breast implant illness sufferers so we have to all question: why?

Why does the FDA allow manufacturers to create a legal shield called pre-emption, exempting them from any liability as the New York Times reported[2] that they're "immune from liability" or accountability as they perform more than 300,000 implant surgeries a year?[4]

How many women have breast implant illness as a result? How many are probably sick and have no clue it's their implants!

All these decades later, the FDA will probably tell you there isn't enough research[5] to prove breast implants cause illness. Yet this is why it's important to support researchers, such as my explant surgeon who we will learn more about in this chapter.

Professor Anand Deva is a fourth generation doctor who is very committed to why him and his family became medical doctors in the first place. He is dedicated to health. Please remember that when you see a cosmetic surgeon, of course they're focused primarily on your aesthetics. We need to educate them more and provide them with more research on how the illness has progressed.

The more research we have, the more we educate the surgeons on a grassroots level. Perhaps, then this will dictate the way in which the FDA handle things.

One can only hope and manifest. It is my wish that they will listen. We are all literally "dying to be well!"

The problems and the breast implant illness is not going away. It only seems to be getting worse. Only recently did Allergen have a total recall of all of their textured products! The company then offered to replace them with a smooth product. Customers are confused and angry. They are told that every time a company recalls a product that there is a safer one, or a better one, and it seems that we are left to discover that these new ones year after year are still creating complications as we continue to report more and more research from participants in implant illness surveys.

In support groups that you will see online on Facebook, or even Instagram, people band together and give each other everything from their own experiences to who they recommend for surgery and what prices we should be looking out for. I saw one woman say, "We are sick, we are angry and we are not going away!"

I think her anger is directed towards the FDA (Food and Drug Administration) predominantly, who she feels, was allowing the perpetual cycle of problems to continue to occur.

Others on the online groups have felt that they have been censored. They have reported that these private groups have had bots and manufacturer spies observing the banter between this growing community of millions. To be accepted in any of the online groups, there are a series of questions and a waiver that needs to be signed. Some support groups even ask for a donation.

As much as it is important to have a support group for us all, I think it's really wise to take these groups with a 'grain of salt' also, because as supportive and informative as they will be, they can also be quite toxic. I must say that before entering any of these groups, there should be a trigger warning, because women do post their before and after photos. When I first observed these support groups, I was very upset because I had still had my implants in and sometimes, this information will either make you see too much surgery, which is quite gruesome, or it can potentially make you feel like you want your implants out right away! You cannot on see the graphic pictures of the blackened or ruptured and moldy implants or the surrounding scar tissue. You also cannot hurry your operation.

Implant companies and manufacturers of breast implants have been going bankrupt, insolvent and shutting shop for many years. In 2016, the company that I bought the product from, Silimed went bankrupt and closed down, and I was not even aware until my explanting surgeon told me after my surgery. In more recent news, Ideal implants[6] are doing the same and one has to wonder is it because of the amount of complications or is it because the amount of women now explant in? Whichever the case, they are the same thing. And one only has to look at the frequency and heist that these companies shut down that will help you to join the dots on how risky these devices really are[7].

Ever noticed one thing that women with breast implants or even those who are subjected to filler and Botox addiction have? In their photos and selfies there, often looking emotionally vacant. There's something missing. They're hyperaware of their exterior being mirrored back to them in a photograph, capturing evidence of who they are in that moment, yet something in there, is missing.

For everyone, what's missing is different. Whatever it is you or they are needing is valid.

We all deserve love and to have our needs met.

It's the impossible beauty standards that women around the world have been subjected to, and know that there is an instant judgment whether it's a subconscious feeling within themselves or a hyper awareness of "comparisonitis,"you will see that women who are being captured in a photograph that used to share their soul, and those who are aware that you were staring at their assets, are two different feelings.

I have seen this in myself. However, there was a time where I forgot that the implants wearing me and I feel like the true essence kept busting to come out. It's because I was someone who wanted to share what I really am on the inside but my armor was blocking who I really am.

It's like that song from "America's Got Talent" Wyn Starks who created a big hit called "who I am". He says "I gotta be me. I gotta be I. I got to be who I know I am inside. I'm finally free. Look at me fly. It's always been there. It just took me a minute to find it. If I were to be anybody else, I'd just be hiding who I am.."

It's our scars and our story that shows us in our essence. It's our wrinkles. It's our pimples. Its our rashes and birthmarks that all make us so gorgeous!

so what is the western world narrative?

I'm observing:

◊ Shame and stigma - "You did this to yourself so why should healthcare cover your mistake?" culture.

◊ Shock and sadness with those who have loved ones with implants. They want to be able to help.

◊ Sufferers are feeling as though they have not been properly informed of the toxic ingredients and risks / surgeons creating repeat business.

◊ Subculture of online support groups on Facebook with hundreds of thousands / millions of women sharing privately and intimately their stories and photographs of suffering or triumphs.

◊ Misinformation due to cosmetic industry protecting itself with conflicting with Doctors and researchers like Dr Tania Ash and Professor Anand Deva who are aware of the commercial aspect and are invested in "duty of care".

◊ The professional industry as a whole is changing their business models with a new demand for explants and with data to support the implants as the inflammatory driver causing 'mast cell activation syndrome'.

◊ Breast implant illness sufferers are expressing what they call "medical gaslighting", because they feel unheard as though their symptoms have not been properly listened to and the medical profession has been denying that breast implant illness is real.

◊ Not all surgeons are recommending or performing a complete or Total Capsulectomy surgery to remove the surrounding tissue.

◊ Breast implant illness is actually an entire systemic response.

◊ New research by breast implant illness expert Dr. Tania Ash presents this as 'mast cell activation syndrome'. It is a cytokine storm.

◊ New data by Professor Anand Deva to support this as a result of witnessing my surgery, has come to fruition.

◊ Not enough trained surgeons to be able to fit in the amount of women that need an operation. Their cost is so extraordinary that the women cannot even afford it so they suffer for many years. They are literally slowly dying.

◊ Implant illness isn't just women who are suffering. Also affected are the trans community and breast cancer survivors with mastectomy who are then implanted with a secondary potentiality to develop another type of breast cancer.

◊ Implant illness is not just in the breasts but can be sufferers with calf implants or other types of implants too.

◊ There are too many undetected ruptures such as my case where six surgeons and an MRI did not pick up the hole in my left implant bag until the operation. New detection equipment is needed and most recently there is something called sonobreasts, operating out of Santa Monica, which can apparently pick up ruptures that an MRI cannot. We need better detection equipment so that we can triage the emergency cases.

◊ The FDA have recently announced about five months ago that the surrounding scar tissue is squamous cell carcinoma and there are new cancers being discovered in the capsule daily.

◊ The recent Allergan recall of all textured products has created another new type of cancer called anaplastic large cell lymphoma (ALCL)

◊ Doctors are pushing for replacement products instead of warning women of the risks and medical doctors such as Dr. Tania Ash are calling out for the TGA to have a black box warning label the way the FDA have this is the only way to create true informed consent.

◊ The question of medical negligence presses with class actions brewing and companies folding due to recalls

◊ The question of silicone vs saline has been sold to us as a narrative that one is better than the other, or that textured vs smooth implants also may be better but year after

year they are all proving toxic and dangerous with mold, bacteria and ruptures or leaks in the valve. It's honestly just a ticking time bomb and just a matter of time.

◊ The way in which this story is told is a holistic approach because we are not just looking at the breasts as the sickness anymore but rather the entire system as though breast implant illness needs a new name now as we finally learn what it truly is

◊ Facebook group culture is purposely created so that it is a closed group with entry only by proof of illness. It is a testament to the audience needing support and growing rapidly without any marketing but rather just word of mouth

◊ Men are also being affected as they learn about their sisters, mothers, girlfriends and friends who are all affected. They want to support women in redefining beauty as they help them to finally address the root cause of why they implanted in the first place

◊ They are horrified at the thought of losing a loved one. Some men have come forward and apologized, or are desperate to educate people they love.

◊ Upsellling of secondary surgeries. It feels like a case of would you like fries with that? The issue with this is that women are holding off their surgery because it becomes a surgery that might take a couple of hours and instead potentially takes four to six hours. That means that they have to try and slot you in to a spot that they may not have. There are a lot more to our slots and it costs a lot less.

Let's get you feeling wonderful biologically and physiologically too!

Detox protocols

You're going to need to do some major detoxing on a physical level as well as your emotional level as you detach from the old you and embrace the new you!

It's pretty exciting actually. There will be tough times as your body purges or tries to find that balance again but I want to get you started.

Just know that many women have had the opportunity to detox and gain their health back and we want you to be one of those too!

I felt very privileged being able to be guided by one of the best medical and integrative doctors who is an expert in breast implant illness, which is as she says, effectively mast cell activation syndrome.

Having this overview understanding of what happens to our bodies when breast implants are in place is crucial, as you start to mop up the mess when you're in an explant stage.

Dr. Tania Ash

Dr. Tania and I have known each other for decades as we have co-managed many in the Australian community when we both ran wellness practices. We appeared on the Australian Today Show just weeks after my explant, and I'm very proud to have her contribution in this chapter.

One of the reasons I chose Dr. Tania Ash to provide us with this chapter is not just because of her knowledge in the area but also because I'm honoring the fact that she too suffered, endured and is now sharing her personal story. I believe this is one of the reasons why this woman is so knowledgeable. She knows firsthand what this is and it's a bittersweet pill to swallow when you have had to go through some thing to be able to so eloquently share it and spare it with others.

"Thank you Andi for inviting me to contribute to your extremely important and timely book and BII/MCAS navigational guide.

I am a doctor of 29 years experience, and I have specialised in Functional Medicine over the past 20 years. I am board certified in Functional Medicine, and my special interest area is Mast Cell Activation Syndrome (MCAS). Patients with chronic fatigue (syndrome) and fibromyalgia typically have MCAS underpinning these symptoms. My clinical practice of Functional Medicine specialising in treating this medically challenging patient community has been significantly honed over the past 20 years, with my ongoing research and education in this area. I also have lifelong genetic MCAS myself, and my first-hand experience is the key reason I became keenly interested in medicine and specifically this condition, and I hence have a deep-seated empathy and compassion for my patients suffering from it.

I first became aware of the diagnosis of MCAS in 2020 from my own focussed research. I had not been taught about this significant medical condition in either medical school, my GP Fellowship, my Functional Medical Fellowship, nor ongoing post-graduate training. MCAS typically has a relapsing and remitting course, and the mast cell reactivity flares with a vast range of precipitants including stress, including trauma which hardwires the sympathetic nervous system, pathogens (chronic viral, bacterial, parasitic and fungal infections), foreign bodies (including surgical implants such as breast implant), electromagnetic radiation (for example mobile phones, wifi, close proximity to telecommunication towers), biotoxins including from environmental mold, (water damaged buildings), toxic heavy metals and pesticides in the food chain contributing to overwhelmed detoxification pathways; hormonal cycles and depletion; as well as fundamental nutrient deficiencies.

Our mast cells are our key first responders of the immune system designed to recognise foreign invaders and rally the immune troops to mount a coordinated immunological response. They occur throughout the body, and are particularly concentrated at mucosal surfaces for protection. As these environmental exacerbants accumulate, they have an aggravating stacking effect on the mast cell reactivity. When mast cell degranulate, they release over 200 different meditators into the blood stream. These include the vast inflammatory cascade such as leukotrienes, cytokines, prostaglandins, tumour necrosis factor, as well as adrenaline and noradrenaline. As a result, the human host can experience a vast array of miscellaneous debilitating symptoms, impacting multiple systems in the body; as well as inducing hypothalamic/pituitary-adrenal (HPA)-ovarian/ testicular axis suppression. The extensive symptoms include such presentations as relapsing/chronic fatigue; rheumatological- fibromyalgic and arthralgic pain; cognitive dysfunction including impaired executive function; psychological symptoms such as anxiety/depression/panic attacks; neurological symptoms such as dysautonomia including postural orthostatic tachycardia syndrome (POTS), migraines; ENT-chronic nasal and sinus congestion, tinnitus; dermatological manifestations including hives, eczema, dermographism; respiratory-asthma, dyspnoea; gastrointestinal disturbances such as reflux and irritable bowel syndrome; haematological eg. thrombocytopaenia, leukopaenia including neutropaenia, anaemia. MCAS is also a significant risk factor for auto-immune diseases.

MCAS patients unfortunately often present to serial medical specialists in the hope of acquiring a definitive diagnosis and tailored treatment, but their symptoms may be unfortunately frequently viewed through the reductionist lens of the subspecialty, rather than corroborating the systemic symptoms in their entirety. There is also still a significant lack of awareness of the diagnosis of MCAS throughout the medical profession- underpinning this frequently overlooked diagnosis.

I have been progressively expanding upon a MCAS treatment protocol over the past three years to augment, strengthen and support the immunological and biochemical body terrain. This includes a low histamine/oxalate/

salicylate diet (further expanding upon the Royal Prince Alfred (RPA) diet); integrating mast cell stabilising foods; mast cell stabilising practitioner supplements; detoxification pathway augmentation practitioner supplements to assist clearance of toxic heavy metals, environmental toxins and biotoxins such as mold biotoxins; environmental awareness education; incorporating a daily parasympathetic practice (to counter sympathetic nervous system dysregulation to lower mast cell reactivity; screening and treating key nutrient deficiencies such as zinc and copper which significantly impact immune regulation and detoxification; medications such as antihistamines, Epipen (if the patient had had associated angio-oedema/ anaphylaxis), and mast-cell stabilising compounded sodium cromoglycate and ketitifen.

In addition, the genetically inherited medical condition, Ehlers-Danlos Syndrome (EDS), has a significant association with MCAS and dysautonomia, frequently occurring as a triad. I am vigilant to be actively looking for this condition in my MCAS patients -and so it is part of my initial MCAS screening questionnaires., imcluding the hypermobile variant. The defective collagen throughout all bodily connective tissues pathognomonic of this condition impairs the barrier function of diverse epithelial linings to protect against foreign bodies/ invading pathogens, as well as an association with impaired antigen presentation in some patients. These impairments cumulatively raise the risk of acute and chronic infections. So I routinely employ nutritional collagen strengthening protocols for this condition to augment the epithelial barriers, as well as nutrients to support the immunological response. I have EDS myself so I am very familiar with managing both it and its associated medical conditions due to the weak defective collagen. I routinely refer my EDS patients and my more severe MCAS patients to the speciality physiotherapist Zebras Australia in Melbourne who are very familiar and experienced with managing both special needs patient communities, with paced gentle strengthening and parasympathetic retraining programmes.

I fundamentally see my job as a health detective with key pattern recognition. When I read Andi's comprehensive health including MCAS questionnaires, including her breast implant history, I was able to hone in on the red flag clues and piece the jigsaw pieces together of BII/MCAS. Finding the right surgeon with extensive awareness of breast implant illness/MCAS and the need for en bloc removal /surrounding tissue dissection to remove toxin laden tissues or silicon spillage-is absolutely fundamental. From here, employing toxin and heavy metal tissue binders such as nano glutathione liver phase 1+2 detox support herbal support such as silymarin, a toxin and heavy metal gut binder such as zeolite,/activated charcoal/silica. I highly recommend the dietary advice on mastcell360.com for a low reactive diet. Natural anti-inflammatory and pain relieving supplements such as curcumin/Boswellia are very helpful and safe. Adopting a daily parasympathetic practice is essential such as breathwork, meditation , yoga, tai-chi, qi-gong-literally rewires the nervous system so that the mast cells are less trigger happy/reactive. Regular chiropractic adjustments definitely assist nervous system dysregulation too.

I absolutely believe we can heal from BII/MCAS. Our bodies have an extraordinary capacity to resolve, dissolve and heal when supported in the right ways.

A combination of all of these interventions, including en bloc removal of my nine year old silicon breast implants with extensive detoxification support, have progressively facilitated me to be living the best health of my life at 53. There is no magic wand, but instead embracing daily healthy patterns for life.

My own lifelong personal health journey inspired me to both pursue medicine and specialise in this all too frequently overlooked and misunderstood area. It is my dharma and life purpose. Educating and raising awareness both in the public arena and within the medical profession is my calling with Andi.

Learning to accept and not shame the perfect cosmetic imperfection of our bodies is also a significant lesson for us all. Learning to be gentle with ourselves is fundamental. Our easiest and best days are when we are in the flow zone. Similarly when our body terrain is balanced, our bodies also are in flow -and balanced self-regulation. Just like optimal organic nutritional nourishment for our bodies, we also need to daily seed inspiring healthy mind wisdom morsels too!"

Some of my favorite supplements I used were things like:

◊ Colloidal Gold (mitochondrial repair)

◊ C60 which is the most powerful antioxidant

◊ Binders like 3i Fulvic and Humic Acid or ones from Cell Core

◊ Intravenous nutrition, including glutothione which is another powerful antioxidant

◊ Turmeric to decrease inflammation

◊ Bone broth to repair the gut and the lining of the tissue in the stomach so that other nutrition can be better assimilated

◊ Probiotics to restore the flora and fauna in the gut and prebiotics to create a healthy home before the probiotics to flourish. Certain foods are good pre-biotics, including garlic, and onion.

◊ Take arnica, orally, or topically, to decrease any bruising and swelling

Low histamine diet

The mast cell activation syndrome diet as Tania mentioned, seems to work for many women or sufferers that have developed an intolerance to foods that are high in histamines.

The challenging thing is that some people react to some foods, and others are fine with all the other foods. There is no 'one size fits all' approach in this low histamine diet. I encourage you to try removing some foods and then re-introducing them to see which ones you are OK with and which ones you may be reacting to.

Posture checks!

Another really great way to get you to repair physically is to remember that you can change the way your chest looks just with posture. Another reason to go and have chiropractic care, or do yoga and have a great ergonomics. Neurological stretches that restore your body's spinal curves are crucial and eventually you will be able to start working the chest again in the gym to strengthen your pectoral muscles. Pectoral rehabilitation can help you create a chest that looks younger or have the breast shape look perkier.

Take your time on all of this because it was only at five months post my surgery that I wanted to even think about working my chest and pectoral muscles with things like bench press.

Listen to your body and you will know along with your healthcare professional when everything feels right for you.

Before going into my surgery though, I had so much chiropractic care in my lifetime. I really think that my body responded well to changing posture immediately. I now stand so much straighter and can breathe so much deeper as a result of having that heavyweight being taken off my chest. This in itself makes my smaller breasts look better.

It's only natural that when we slouch forward everything hangs down, including the way, our stomach looks. Changing your posture actually changes the way you perceive the world too. It's through your nervous system that you perceive the world, adapt to stress and coordinate all bodily functions.

Go gently...

Just like you will go slowly with your physical therapy, you will also need to go slow with your detoxifying. With regards to any kind of detoxing from something that is toxic, it may take several weeks, if not months, and potentially even a year before your body can get back to homeostasis again. I have observed that after an explant, many have come forth to me and have expressed how upset they have been that they have not fully recovered straight away.

Please be gentle with yourself and understand that as cliché as it sounds healing really does take time. Because most of us feel so elated and light and free as soon as our implants are removed, we expect the rest of our symptoms to go away just as quick.

Please note that this is an allopathic way of thinking. Allopathy is a medical model, whereby it is a mechanistic approach and not holistic. The wellness model is holistic and acknowledges that everything is connected, and to address it naturally, we need to get everything working in concert with each other again just like a really finely tuned orchestra.

And as a result, you may have some other issues that need to be addressed in concert with something else.

Take, for example, hair loss. I suffered a lot of hair loss and instead of thinking that because your hair has an improved as a result of the implants being removed, you may need to address the other health challenges that this inflammatory driver created. It's not going to be one magic health supplement that you can take that is good for hair growth. You may need to address the reason why nutrition has being pulled away from the area of providing it to the hair and to your other areas of infection and inflammation. Addressing it all holistically will give you a maximum results for overall well-being and wellness. Take this philosophy for anything that you are wanting to heal and improve.

The body is always working to heal. We just need to give it the right environment and have patience and work with it. Take for example the fact that we are getting new cells every second of every day. We are replenishing. It's the quality of those cells that are what I am interested in. That's why all of my wellness practices are done so that when I'm replacing cells, I am making sure that they are working in a way to create the healthiest cells that my body can design. Just like you wouldn't put braces on your teeth for just one week and take them off and expect your teeth to be straight, same with anything that you're trying to improve in your body.

Nervous systems have a memory, and eventually will remember what it felt like to be in good health again.

Professor Anand Deva said in a recent interview, "Chronic inflammation drives disease. An implant goes into the patient and for whatever reason the body tries to fight against it." He then went on to say "I think all women who have breast implants will have an issue at some point."

Just because the data doesn't point to an immediate reaction or illness to your implants doesn't mean you weren't injured. It's a build up effect. "We need long term studies" he said as he urged women to send in their statistics.

There's still so much research to be done, and I managed to get these stats in fact from his office:

◊ We currently have over 400 women who have registered in our National BII Study.

◊ In Australia, there are approximately 20,000 people who have breast implants inserted each year (75% cosmetic, 25% reconstructive). In the most recent ABDR report, it stated for 2021, there were 12,303 patients, using 23,500 implants added to the registry in that year.

◊ Page 4 of the latest Australian Breast Device Registry annual report states 'ABDR data continues to show a decline in the proportion of inserted devices, and an increase in the number of revisions and explants. Removal of devices without replacement (ie explant) increased by 4% for reconstructive patients and 7.9% for cosmetic patients from 2016 to 2021.'

◊ On page 24 and page 25 of the ABDR annual report the increase in explants for reconstructive patients in 2016 explant was 1.3%, in 2021 is 5.3%, increase of 4%, a four fold increase. The increase in explants for augmentation patients = in 2016 explant was 0.6%, in 2021 is 8.5%, increase of 7.9%, a 14 fold increase

◊ Breast Implants are Class III medical devices (same as pacemakers, defibs) which are defined by the FDA as "usually sustain or support life, are implanted or present a potential unreasonable risk of illness or injury."

◊ In 2021, the FDA issued guidance for manufacturers to improve patient information including a new black box warning. But women don't normally get to open the box their implants come in so they are not privy to the warnings.

◊ It is very hard to find information about implant complication rates. Patients need to go to their implant manufacturer and sift through pages of information to find this data.

◊ The Natrelle Saline-filled implant patient checklist is a good example of the sort of information patients can read. On page 9 of this document, it states the long-term risks patients experiencing capsular contracture are 51.7% and for rupture, is 22.5%.

◊ In the Allergen silicone implant pamphlet[9], the complication rated moderate, severe, or very severe (excludes mild and very mild ratings). For reoperation, implant removal or replacement, implant rupture, implant extrusion, and pneumothorax all occurrences are included, regardless of severity.

◊ There were no reports of the following complications: irritation, lymphadenopathy, lymphedema, palpable orientation mark, pneumothorax

◊ Other complications include joint swelling, implant movement, bottoming out, tear in the capsule, skin indentation and synmastia

◊ Other complications not listed above have also been reported in patients with breast implants. These include:

◊ Breastfeeding difficulties

◊ Calcium deposits

◊ Breast tissue atrophy/chest wall deformity

◊ Connective Tissue Disease (CTD)

◊ CTD signs and symptoms

◊ Neurological Disease

◊ Neurological Signs and Symptoms

◊ Cancer

◊ Lymphoma, including Anaplastic Large Cell Lymphoma or ALCL

◊ Suicide

◊ Potential effects on offspring

◊ On the Mentor implant website, they state 'The health consequences of a ruptured silicone gel breast implant has not been fully established.'

◊ On the Natrelle implant website, they state 'Patients receiving breast implants have reported a variety of systemic symptoms, such as joint pain, muscle aches, confusion, chronic fatigue, autoimmune diseases, and others. Individual patient risk for developing these symptoms has not been well established. Some patients report complete resolution of symptoms when the implants are removed without replacement.'

◊ The FDA published data on the breast implant 'device reports' they received from women suffering with systemic symptoms related to their implants.

≡ SURGICALTIMES Q

In 'Paradigm Shift,' Google Search Volume for 'Breast Implant Removal' Up 235%, for 'Explant' Up 527%

Google Trends Highlights a Breast Implant Paradigm Shift, Plastic and Reconstructive Surgery: February 28, 2022 – Volume – Issue – 10.109

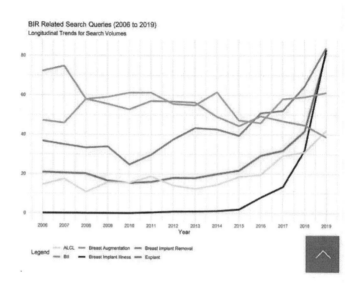

This isn't a joke! I made a mistake. I didn't research and read fine print.

Now I am. Now was a little too late. I had to forgive myself. I don't judge others or try to change what I did but the truth needs to be told. Implants are creating more illness than you know. We can only look forward and start to prepare to facilitate a natural and healthy environment to thrive in, because these silicon or saline bags are a ticking time bomb and you won't know when they switched or what your entire system is doing to keep you surviving. From mold, to bacteria, contracture and undetected ruptures or the textures creating new types of breast cancers, at what cost are you hanging on?

Goodbye bags! Let's bust out!

If you're not ready for this next chapter, then please take your time and pick it up again when you have a surgery date in place or after you have had your operation. The aim of this is to give you a visual on what you're brand new well life is going to look like.

Chapter 6

Bust Out The Empowered You!

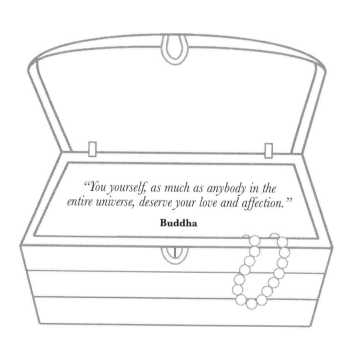

"You yourself, as much as anybody in the entire universe, deserve your love and affection."

Buddha

It's time to 'bust out' of any stigma, expectations and labels or stories that have been owning you and transform you to an newer version of yourself.

This new story explores your past inner dialogue you didn't realize was subliminally programming. You'll release anything else that has been holding you back from being your most empowered self.

For those who still remain attached to their breast implants, I completely understand that this choice to augment and stay augmented has served you in becoming the most empowered person that you know right now.

The 'now' is actually all we have.

I was there too. I didn't plan for this in my future.

I think the pressing thing is that when we sign up for this procedure, we don't plan for what is going to come. At least you're now more aware.

I totally relate to all of it. I felt like a new version of me with my breast implants, and I really felt at the time, that it took me to another level of confidence.

The confidence was reflected in my professional world which had applauded my new look as I'm in an industry where my appearance is judged. Ironically, it didn't change my wellness career, it actually elevated it.

In hindsight, I often think it had to do with my attitude towards it. Having said that, my shedding with the explant has taken this audience and fanbase to a whole new level now.

On another level, personally, and psychologically too, it emanated on and had an effect on my dating life also.

I never knew that when I would prepare to explant though, that I'd be able to not only maintain that confidence, but actually transcend onto a whole new level.

That's the beauty of evolution. You don't realize when you hit that height that there would be a new height, until after the fact.

So take the plunge and dive right in my dear. Growth can be painful. Trust me, I know!

My whole being in this new, "original me" body with more wisdom, helped me to transcend into somebody I always subconsciously imagined but never knew it was possible. I so want this for you. And when you are ready, I am so here for you.

To get myself to this state of mind and to help you understand where this all comes from, I want you to soak in the notion that humans are wired to synchronize.

We are wired to want to be the same or feel safe in familiarity. Sometimes we break out and break free but essentially we are also pack animals. Just like dogs are happier and healthier when they are in a pack, so too are humans, happier and healthier, just like these pack animals.

As a wellness expert, I often researched synchronicity that would happen with healing. I didn't have to go too far to realize that it was all staring at me in my face when it came to how we function or heal that is so connected to one another. Take for example, women who live together for a period of time or spend time together. Often, they start to synchronize their menstrual cycles. Men may not know this, but one woman could be cycling her menstruation at the beginning of the month, and the other woman, maybe in the middle of the month, but when they start to spend time together, eventually, these two women will start and finish their period or menstrual cycle on the exact days together!

When birds fly in a flock or fish in that same triangular formation, when one turns left, they all turn left maintaining that beautiful formation of togetherness. No words need to be shared. It's not like the fish or bird at the front who is leading, turns around and says to the others, "Hey mate! In 50 metres, we are all going to turn left!" They just know. Synchronicity in healing, and how we work is something to note. The message I draw from this is how not only are we designed to be the same and wired to synchronize, but knowing this means that if we are steered onto a dangerous path, it can be used for the not so greater good.

When I was shopping around this book and idea to production companies, in order to create a documentary series about this subject, I was asked what the national narrative was around this topic.

It got me thinking about how a producer is one to share, learn and push an agenda that the collective are already engaged in. Another terminology, for this could be described as the word and term "trending". You may have heard of it being used in the social media realm where we want to learn which kinds of posts and content is trending. Which is most popular is what advertisers want to invest in. I remember a famous quote by Walt Disney himself. He said, "You don't build it for yourself. You know what the people want and you build it for them."

Everything I have ever created and everything that I have done professionally was because the people guided me. This very book has not been an easy one to write but I built it for you and I created it for the collective who in this very timely fashion needed me and these words.

However, let's now turn our faces towards that warm sunlight in the hope that the rays and the vitamin D, that nourishes and penetrates our skin, heals our every system as it sends the ability for other nutrition, to be absorbed, just like having a deeper understanding of this new way of looking at your chest, your 'treasured chest', will help you to heal so many other areas of your life. At the very least though, it will give you more of an insight. Just like art, your interpretation is what counts and that's what you will receive from it.

So let me know help you interpret the point to this story. What do the terms national narrative and trending have to do with anything wellness or busting out to feel empowered? Well, the reality is that because as humans are wanting to be the same and synchronize, it is in my hope and wish that we will also synchronize and help each other to heal from the toxins. We are allowed for so long. Instead of being the same with these foreign objects, we will now be the same with the sharing of one very incredibly near commonality, and that is our explant scars.

It is with the scars that we will be reminded of our power. This is exactly why I chose to show them off in this very book. Before I ask explanted, I really thought that I would hate my scars and feel triggered or traumatized every time I would look at them in the mirror but I was honestly so surprised at how immediately I loved them. Just like when a mother births her baby, and she stares at the baby for the first time, she is immediately in love with her child, which is a part of her.

My scars are a part of me and my story and your scars are a part of you and your story and that's what makes you so beautiful because our stories are who we are. Who you are is good. Who you are is beautiful. Who you are is unique. Who you are is everything that this world needs. As I share these words my eyes well with tears because you know that not enough people speak in this fashion, and we need to hear it more.

You might want to join many of the class actions. Although I have heard that it seems almost impossible to win. You might like to find a way to win in your own special way. Whilst it would be important to be remunerated, it's also important to take charge of your health because that wealth is worth more than anything. Exposing and documenting and sharing and supporting others is also another way of winning. Justice isn't always just. You need to find your own way potentially to put your story to rest.

Daily practice exercises

Mirror work

Coming to terms with your new self is something that needs to be practiced daily. And doing the spiritual work can emanate into flowing and having a flow on affect in other areas of your life. I believe that positive affirmation done in front of the mirror is very powerful. You may choose to look in your eyes and at your scars or your body and love that person that you see as the person that has endured trauma or just needed more love at the time. Hold that little child and angel who is now an adult and tell this person all the things that you love about them.

Start your sentences with this phrase and every time you add a new sentence. This is the beginning to all your sentences done in the mirror.

"What I love about you is…"

Make sure that the things you are loving are not aesthetic only. Make sure that you are talking about strength of character and other attributes that are focused on who you are as a person and why we love having you in this world.

Supplements

Please remember that you will be taking a myriad of supplements or having intravenous, infusions and beautiful, healthy organic foods. This is a period of your life where you may be supplementing, because your body was missing out on nutrition as it was drawing nutrition from a triage perspective to the area of the infection site. To supplement means that you are supplementing nutrition where your body didn't receive it before. I believe that supplements should not be taken forever, and please work with your natural healthcare practitioner of choice to make sure that you are receiving practitioner, strength, supplementation, and for the reason that your supplementation can be monitored by that health professional. For example, if you are taking wormwood for a parasitic, gut cleanse, you may need to do this periodically, and have breaks in between.

You will never need to take one supplement for the rest of your life and our aim is to help you get nutrition from food eventually. It's all about assimilation of nutrition and creating a body that is in balance, so that you are operating with optimal health and assimilating nutrition that you're having from your healthy meals.

Movement is life

As a certified wellness coach, people often ask me, "What's the best exercise to do?" I will always reply that it is the one you love the most. It really doesn't matter what kind of exercise you do, as long as you do it! For some people, it might be dancing and others it could be surfing, swimming, martial arts, hiking or anything that makes you feel alive and excited when you're moving your body. This needs to be a daily practice. We are not designed to be sedentary. Having said that a daily practice needs to be done with care post surgery. You will need to talk to your surgeon and doctor about when you can start to move fully again. Remember, though that movement is life and if you don't move it, you lose it! Doing very gentle movement in the beginning is key as you owner of your body and get it back to health.

Proper hydration

We must flush toxins out of our bodies and to do that, our bodies need quality water. We are not drinking enough water, and our water quality has been polluted with forever chemicals or toxins, and sometimes spoiled with phytoestrogen as a result of being transported in plastics.

I highly recommend that you install a Complete Home Filtration system in your home to have pure and clean water in every tap including the one that you bath and shower in. Mention me and they will probably look after you!

For the period of time that you are detoxing post surgery, I highly recommend that you invest in water that you know will replenish your cells. The purest water I have found is from the Austrian Alps. My friends at Hallstein Water would be happy to look after you if you mention my name and this book. I've actually never tasted water so pure because it is pure. It's a literally straight from the Austrian Alps and transported into a glass order a bottle. It's an investment I like to make when doing a proper cleanse.

Be gentle!

Healing expectations after explants:

There seems to be this idea that having an explant is going to be a miracle cure! You may not wake up feeling instantly amazing. Most of us do feel miraculously better but some of us will need to take time to heal. It's important to have realistic expectations and be gentle with yourself.

Healing from any surgery is going to be a lot on your body. There's going to be a recovery from the exhaustion, the inability to move, the medication and anesthetic that you have had and it is very reasonable for you to not feel the same for about two months.

Be careful of comparing yourself to somebody else's journey and be aware that each person is unique and therefore their healing journey will be varied to yours. Nonetheless, they were going to be some adjuncts that you can do to fast track the healing, and that is in the detoxing suggestions as well as all of these paragraphs prior.

As your body will begin detoxing naturally after explanting, symptoms come and go so you may like to journal it.

Sometimes people can feel worse as they are expelling toxins so it's important to note those times and allow yourself to have deep rest too. This is all so normal as the body works to expel toxins.

Your detoxing period will vary depending on how long you've had your breast implants and if you had previous illnesses, or if you had a rupture or leak. Sometimes you may have had devices that were recalled and the exterior fuzzy layer may take some time to detox from your body.

Research your device!

It's important to find out the health ramifications, risks and damages your breast implants have from your manufacturer. Continue to check in on your health with your health practitioner, legal team and anyone else that may need to help you. Please do monitor it all closely.

As you are incorporating these daily practices and educating and empowering yourself with knowledge, please know that you are not alone. For this very reason, I have decided to include other people's stories, so that you can connect with them by reaching out or just reading their contribution in this next chapter.

We all have the ability to overcome anything, but we are stronger in numbers. You are so important in this movement. Because you are now and educated reader, I urge you to pay it forward and educate others with this knowledge. You may like to gift your book to somebody else once you have read it.

Congratulations on getting through it all this far!

Chapter 7

Be-YOU-tiful stories to inspire

"Half the healing is in the hearing."

Andi Lew

"Half the healing is in the hearing."

Andi Lew

These are the "forgotten women" who wanted to share their stories with you so that everyone feels less alone and feels heard which is part of the healing process.

Duke University researchers note an "'explosion" of public interest in breast implant removal and explant surgery. Interest they say represents a "paradigm shift". This was published in the SURGICAL TIMES - March 4, 2022

Here's the explosion that's appearing everywhere - in various books, documentaries, news shows, social media platforms, and now with this final chapter. I celebrate women who wanted to contribute their stories so that you can help them to feel good too. Mostly these contributors wanted to help others in the exact same way that I do. With a 527% increase in searching for 'explant', on line, it's obvious that awareness is growing.

Sarah's Story:

"I was once quite happy and comfortable living the conventional life, but I began to look at things very differently when my body started failing me after getting breast implants and I had to take on the battle of figuring out what the heck was going on!

A little background - I was REALLY into fitness; some might even say "obsessed". It started with P90x, which led to body building. I hired a trainer who solely worked with bikini competitors to help me get into the best shape of my life at 30. I didn't want to compete; I just wanted "the look", and with that came my push for breast implants and the deterioration of my health.

Since I was very young, I had always wanted bigger breasts. I can pinpoint the exact moment in my young life when breasts became important to me. When I was around ten years old, someone very important in my life

said, "you're going to be 4ft 11in like me, but don't worry, you'll have 'the Johnson boobs'". It was this pivotal moment that changed everything regarding body image for me. Large breasts became important. This memory drove my desire, but it was my newfound fitness lifestyle that finally led to making the big decision to get the breasts that I thought I needed to feel beautiful and worthy.

Within about six months of getting breast implants, I began to see my once "perfect health" (I say "perfect" because I had a terrible diet but zero symptoms of any kind) steadily decline. I began to experience fatigue, irritability, anxiety, feeling cold when no one else was, easy weight gain, brain fog, inability to focus on I was reading, severe fatigue and irritability after exercise, dry skin, loss in sex drive and forgetfulness. I knew something was wrong because I was no longer myself.

As time passed, symptoms worsened. I began experiencing night sweats, horrific insomnia, mind racing, perioral dermatitis, headaches, food sensitivities, chemical sensitivity, heart palpitations, periods of tachycardia when at rest, and extreme anxiety to the point of not wanting to be in public. I couldn't tolerate loud sounds or bright lights and being at work in a noisy environment with everyone chit-chatting around me was pure torture. I experienced chest tightness, shallow breathing, and a real fun one, mental awareness of every single breath I took.

I began having menstrual periods that started out with vomiting, explosive diarrhea, and excruciating pain... all at the same time. I had to take oxycodone just to get relief. This led to planning my work schedule around my menstrual cycle. I had no idea what was wrong with me. I was a mess and I felt completely alone. No one understood what I was going through because on the outside I looked fine.

Beyond what I was personally going through, this struggle put a huge strain on my marriage as well. It's so hard to cope with a spouse who suddenly from what seems like out of nowhere becomes this sick. I am very blessed to have a loving and supportive husband but it was still a strain on our relationship. How we feel tends to express itself in how we treat others. There were times I was just not a nice person to be around. Period.

From here, I started having IBS symptoms: bloating, gas, frequent stools, loose stools, and PAIN every evening. It was to the point of not wanting to do anything social because I was so uncomfortable.

Living in my body was so uncomfortable that there were times I literally just wanted to jump outside of my skin and hide under a rock. The discomfort was maddening. I started to wonder if I was just going to have to learn to live with all the symptoms. I'm pretty sure everyone I knew thought I was crazy.

Fast forward to keep a long story short, it took me about five years to finally decide to explant. I did everything I could to restore my health without removing my implants. That got me about 50% better but it wasn't enough. I finally realized that if I ever wanted to fully restore my health, I was going to have to go further upstream to the root causes. The tipping point for me was struggling with fertility and I knew I needed to get the implants out. They were fueling the fire inside my body.

I explanted in 2017 and couldn't be happier with this decision. It wasn't an overnight fix for me. It took a long time to feel optimal again, but I got there through a lot of deep physical and emotional work.

There were so many growth lessons along this journey and I am truly grateful for it. Two of these were getting to the root cause of why I felt I needed breast implants in the first place and understanding who I truly am at my core. It's so incredibly freeing and beautiful to no longer need external validation from others. Who I am is rooted in my relationship with God and how I show up in the world and treat others. This growth led to launching the Life Beyond explant Movement: from pain to empowerment.

Two additional blessings came from this experience. Firstly, my husband and I allowed it to drive us closer together rather than apart. We went through a lot together and we're more connected than ever before. Adversity can do that. And secondly, it has taught me how I should be living in order to keep my health for life.

I hope it encourages you to remain hopeful if you're not seeing immediate improvement in your symptoms after explant. Healing is absolutely possible. I am proof of that. Remember, there is always purpose in our pain. What is yours?

Sarah Phillipe, BSN, FDN-P,
Board Certified Holistic Health Practitioner,
Cellcore Practitioner,
Breast Implant Illness & Detox Expert
http://reversingbreastimplantillness.com

Satin's Story:

Hello Andi!

Thank you so very much for the opportunity to share my story.

Three years ago (left side of photo) I was at my absolute worst health. I was sick in countless areas of my body while caring for my mother who was dying from cancer.

Today (right side of photo) my heart is filled with the deepest of gratitude for the health I have now regained! No more migraines, extreme fatigue, major gut issues, brain fog and trouble articulating my thoughts and words, trouble focusing, weight gain, hormone imbalance, cystic acne and the list goes on! I didn't just remove my breast implants, I put in the hard work to learn my body- what it wants and needs as well as what it doesn't like or can't have. I pushed through the hard days of pain and discouragement, pressing on and pushing myself to stay the course.

I've been taking cellcore supplements. I use red light therapy. I have done visceral manipulation therapy with Jason Racca and breath work with Kimberly Rose and all the things necessary to detox my body and heal it from the inside out.

The journey has been hard but never ever did I think of giving up! God blessed me with an amazing husband who has supported me every single step of the way! I am grateful to have a Practitioner in Sarah Phillipe of Reversing Breast Implant Illness @ reversingbreastimplantillness who validated my struggle and took me as a client, teaching me how to listen to my body and heal it! Never have I ever worked with a practitioner who cares as deeply about their clients as Sarah does. She poured so much into my healing journey and I couldn't be more appreciative of all she taught me!

Before

After

I'm not done yet! I am still healing and learning, but man do I feel amazing! I am so proud of my progress and can't wait to see what the next three years of my health journey looks like!

Thank you to my husband Tyler Pelfrey for being my biggest cheerleader during all this and never giving up on me or us! I love you so much!! Thank you to my best friend Melissa for listening to me whine about my struggles while encouraging me to continue on! I am immensely grateful to be where I am today!"

Satin Pelfrey

www.satinpelfrey.com

BREAST IMPLANTS TOOK A DECADE OF MY LIFE.

Kim Barden's Story:

"They took everything from me, including friends and my own family. No one knows how debilitating this illness is unless they have lived it.

I've been in the BII community since 2015 when there were less than 2000 women who found each other on a Facebook group "Breast Implant Illness and Healing by Nicole." Finding that group saved my life.

At the time of explant, I was 52 years old and at year 14 with Saline Smooth McGhan implants. On December 5, 2015, I had my "light bulb" moment. I will remember that day for the rest of my life because that's the day I learned there was hope after a decade of trauma and debilitating illnesses. At the end, I felt like I was going to die every day and I wanted to. I was no longer functioning and nothing in my body worked any longer. It was 14 years of slowly being poisoned to death. My entire body suffered from head to toe, inside and out.

My story of BII began in 2001. I was a 38 year old single mother, had a great job and purchased my own home in Calabasas, California. After growing up in a low income family in a small midwest town and a lot of physical abuse from early relationships, I wanted more out of life. I left, moved to LA and worked hard to make a good life for myself.

I was thriving and I had everything I ever wanted… until I decided to fix that one thing I hated.. my tubular breasts.

I couldn't even look at my breasts and was mortified for anyone else to see them. I had never seen anyone with breasts as weird as mine and the internet wasn't anything like it is today. I lived in the plastic surgery capital of the world and decided to treat myself to a "LIFT".

I chose a well known Beverly Hills surgeon to consult with. I was very excited for the appointment to finally get my breasts fixed. At the consult, I was surprised when he suggested implants as the best option due to the amount of skin I had. He said there would be less scarring as the incisions would be in the nipples and the implants would fill them up and I would be thrilled. I had zero knowledge on breast implants as they were never on my radar. He was adamant that the results would be much better and recommended Saline Implants because they were 100% safe and would last a lifetime! He's an expert and I know he wouldn't suggest something that would hurt me.. right? I completely trusted his recommendation and agreed to the augmentation. I booked the surgery right then.

I was never thrilled with the implants. My areolas were huge, scarred, lost all sensitivity and I still needed a strong underwire bra. I kept them hidden away as I did prior to augmentation because they still sagged. Huge waste of eight thousand dollars. I definitely would have been happier with the lift that I originally wanted. I didn't question the surgeon at my post op appointments because he said they looked great. I respected this man so much that I thought something was wrong with me for not liking them. I decided that I'm stuck with them since he said I would be buried with them someday. I moved on with life and never thought much about them again ... until they almost killed me.

The first year was ok. By years two and three, I slowly began to deteriorate but never considered a correlation. Fatigue was the first symptom as I remember going to my car and sleeping on my lunch breaks. I never thought much of it. Single mom, crazy work hours. I was a busy lady and I was simply tired. I went to my PC and was diagnosed with Hypothyroidism so I now had an excuse for being over tired. I was put on medication to control it but still needed those daily naps to get through my shifts. After another year later in 2004, I sold my home, left the best job I ever had, and moved to another state where I could afford to support my son and me. I was struggling to get through the days and I had to find a way to work less hours. I was 41 and thought I was just getting older and this was normal. I would be told numerous times over the next decade that I was "probably" experiencing perimenopause.....Must be normal.

Arm pain / ankle stiffness: Over the next couple of years (years four and five with implants), the symptoms increased little by little. The next problem to get my attention was sharp pain deep in my arm that woke me up at night. It occurred every night and was in the same spot. I thought for sure I had bone cancer or something. After at least six months of this, I had X-rays and eventually an MRI which showed nothing. Along with this, I was experiencing fairly extreme morning ankle stiffness. It would take a while before I could walk straight. My job required being on my feet during the majority of my shifts so that is how I justified this issue...must be normal.

Neck: The next problem was my neck. It ached 24 x 7. I was seeing a chiropractor for adjustments and acupuncture every four to five weeks and paying out of pocket because insurance didn't cover. It was the only thing that seemed to help but only for a short period. Every few months, my neck would lock up and I couldn't move. It was extremely painful and a steroid pack and shot would get me moving. I went to a neurosurgeon, had an MRI and was diagnosed with degenerative bulging discs and foraminal spinal stenosis at C5-6-7. So there was an excuse for this too. The spinal stenosis was on the right side yet the excruciating pain was always the Left which happens to be the side of my body that suffered the most when I had implants. This became debilitating over the years with numerous epidural injections, physical therapy and continued monthly chiropractor visits so I could keep working. I was physically tossed around like a rag doll by an abusive boyfriend when I was in my 20's so I decided that this must be normal.

Next was the left shoulder… Onto an Orthopedic shoulder specialist. An MRI indicated degenerative impingement and bone spurs. I had quarterly rounds of cortisone injections in my shoulder which got me through the next several years. The surgeon I was seeing suggested I go ahead and have shoulder surgery to put me out of my misery. Two weeks before the surgery, I ended up with Frozen Shoulder. If you've had that, you know how awful it is. The surgeon was going to continue with the surgery even while it was frozen. A friend suggested I seek a second opinion. I made an appointment with the best in town and his words "you cannot have surgery on a frozen shoulder or you may never come out of the frozen state". I canceled the original surgery and went through six months of physical therapy to get my arm moving again. Again, all out of pocket expenses. I continued on with injections to keep the pain under control because I had so many other issues going on. I assumed this was all from the physical abuse and.... must be normal.

Wrists: may have been the most painful thing to deal with because the slightest movement would send shockwaves through my body. Some days nothing, other days I would be in tears with the slightest movement. I couldn't pick up anymore than a coffee cup without pain. I saw two orthopedic hand surgeons for this over the years because it too became a debilitating factor in my life. After two MRIs, both surgeons diagnosed a rare bone disease call "Keinbocks". I was hoping it was Carpal Tunnel which could have been an easy fix. Both surgeons offered surgery but there were no guarantees and both said it could end up worse. With that option, I had continued with quarterly cortisone injections which gave me some relief for a couple of weeks. They became so painful that from 2011 to explant in 2016, I wore metal plated wrist braces 24 x 7. I only removed them to shower. This deeply impacted my quality of life. Obviously, I blamed the physical abuse on this too... must be normal.

Knees: 1st Orthopedic knee surgeon that ordered the MRI said it wasn't all that bad but suggested he go in orthoscopically and clean the arthritis out. I went to another for a second opinion and was told they were not that bad and shouldn't have any type of surgery. I stuck with ortho #2 and started cortisone injections in my knees. They certainly felt bad to me. It was hard to walk. I ended up in metal plated knee braces (just like the wrists), all day - every day for 5 years. It was awful. Once again, I blamed the physical abuse. Must be normal.

Breast swelling: The biggest red flag during my 14 years should have been in 2010 (9 years in), my left breast swelled up to double its size and stayed that way for eight weeks. My Ogbyn sent me to a general surgeon and a plastic surgeon for their opinions. The mutually made decision was to have surgery to remove the swollen lymph nodes to check for cancer. The outcome was not surprising "you're fine and your implants are in perfect condition". The swelling eventually went down but that breast remained tender and hot to the touch for several years. The doctors never suggested the implants could be a problem so I just moved on thinking ....must be normal.

While dealing with the debilitating issues listed above, there were many more issues slowly taking over my life. There was always something wrong with me. I was constantly dealing with a random problem and going from doctor to doctor. I was no longer able to work full time and the "part" time that I was at work, I wasn't very productive. I worked in commission sales and went from making a very good living to just making a living. I was in my prime but sick all the time. I really did feel like I was dying and my brain wasn't fully functioning. I was becoming a shell of the lively energetic woman that used to handle it all.

By the time I was 48 (10 years with implants), my 88 year old grandmother functioned in a much more productive way than I did in every aspect. Mentally and physically.

The rest of the symptoms that started from time to time to being full on 24 x 7:

My left hip had a non stop dull ache that eventually hurt with every step I took. I ended up donating my bicycle and elliptical because I couldn't use either one. Bone scan showed Osteopenia in my left hip. So here I go again… must be normal.

Monthly cycles became unbearable and unpredictable. I would be out of commission for days at a time in ridiculous pain. I never called in sick for a cycle until I had BII. I was sent to a specialist who recommended Endometrial Ablation. I had that done and the cycles stopped completely which was great. Considered this part of the peri-menopause I was repeatedly told I probably had. This must be normal.

Low blood pressure/chest pains/heart palpitations: I had several ER visits due to chest pains and passing out from maintaining a low blood pressure. But there were never any real answers. I was always sent home and told nothing was wrong. I was eventually put on Midodrine by my oncologist to keep the blood pressure up. My husband took me to the ER so frequently that it became normal practice to drop me off at the entrance and pick me up in the rear parking lot where he would find me laying in the grass.

COPD/breathing problems: By the time I got to year 12 with implants, I was having trouble breathing and saw a pulmonary specialist who diagnosed me with chronic COPD and asthma. CT Scan indicated my lungs were full of blebs (described as little holes). It became so bad that within a year, I struggled to bend over and put my own socks on. I struggled to breathe. Attempted numerous very expensive medications that were not covered by insurance but nothing helped. In the fall of 2015, (year 14 with implants) at 52 years old, the pulmonary suggested an oxygen tank after no improvement from the medications. I am a former smoker so there was a reason for this too. Must be normal.

White blood count: I was referred to an Oncologist because my White Blood Count stayed at and above 24,000 for over six months. I was diagnosed with Hemochromatosis which is too much iron in the blood. There was never an answer found for the high WBC. I was the healthiest sick person my doctors have seen. Must be normal.

Sinusitis/ esophagus / voice box nodules/ vocal cord disfunction / reflux: I spent years going to an ENT for many issues. My nose and head was so congested in the mornings that I couldn't breathe. I continually had sinus infections. I tried numerous expensive allergy meds with zero relief. My voice sounded horse and I was constantly clearing my throat and sniffling. It felt like a had a blockage in my sinuses. I called them "balls of snot" It was gross and painful. I also struggled to get food down. It felt like everything I consumed would get stuck in the esophagus. It hurt and was extremely uncomfortable. Lots of testing, poking and prodding down my nose and throat. I was diagnosed me with Gerd, chronic sinusitis and vocal cord disfunction. Medications did nothing to help any of this. I guess this is normal too. I'm incredibly unlucky to have all these issues.

Tinnitus, dry hair/mouth/eyes: cystic acne, libido 100% gone. Hands and feet always extremely cold under any conditions. I wore long johns under my clothes everyday and live in florida. I could not get warm. I had a weird body odor that would not go away no matter how many showers i took. I had a constant metal taste in my mouth.

I lost all sense of smell and taste. My skin and scalp broke out in sores that wouldn't heal. My gums began deteriorating and my teeth started rotting. I've had nine root canals and most have been extracted for failing. My scalp, eyebrows and eyelashes had large gaps that would not fill in. I moved the part in my hair so my bangs would cover my LEFT eyebrow and cheek. That side of my face was drooping and PC said it was most likely Bells Palsy.

Noise and light sensitivity to where I avoided the outdoors. I couldn't handle bright light, the sounds of people talking or even music.

UTIS, kidney and yeast infections. I had Monistat and Pyridium on monthly auto ship from Amazon. The yeast and UTI's just never went away. After eating, my stomach would bloat and often would be bent over in pain. Terrible constipation.

I had non stop vertigo/dizziness. I felt like I was super drugged or drunk. I could sleep 20 hours a day and it still wasn't enough.

Taking a shower seriously felt like I had run a marathon. My hair became extremely dry and felt almost like hay. My skin dry, face peeling and fingernails were covered in white dry spots.

If I put on 14K gold earrings, my earring holes would fill with pus within minutes. (this is still the case today). A 14k chain on my neck turns my skin black (still does to this day). I react to adhesive elastic in underwear, bathing suits, socks... all elastics continue to irritate my skin.

Cognitive function was gone by year 10. I lived in a constant state of confusion. I struggled to comprehend and follow conversations. I stuttered and slurred like I was under the influence. I could no longer follow a movie, comprehend a book or do basics like sort laundry or prepare a simple meal. Everything was confusing and it was as if I forgot how to do things I've done all my life. I no longer cooked or shopped because I was too confused to make or follow a list. I would get lost in stores that I had shopped in for years. I had a great deal of trouble driving. I would easily become lost and I couldn't make decisions on when it was safe to make a turn or change lanes. When I did attempt to talk, I stuttered and slurred my words. I couldn't remember simple words or the names of friends and family. I was not functioning and became incapable of handling or coping with daily life.

My 23 year old son was on the front lines in Afghanistan the summer of 2014. He was stationed at the Kabul Airport which was a constant target of attack. He would Skype me every Sunday morning and I tried to hide my issues. I couldn't burden him with what was going on with me. I didn't even know what was going on with me and I sure wasn't going to tell him that his mother was dying. On our calls, I could always hear bombing sounds in the background. I couldn't take it. I couldn't contain the tears. I would lose it, I couldn't talk and I would cry uncontrollably. Understandably, the calls became less frequent. I was his only parent and mentally incapable of being the support he needed. This will haunt me the rest of my life. He did return home safe, sound and a decorated war veteran. Thank God. I'm so proud of him.

I am not exaggerating when I say I stopped functioning. I stopped leaving my house except for Dr's appts. I stopped attending parties, wedding and even funerals. My *grandmother died at 91 in 2013 and I was too sick to travel out of state to her funeral. I lived with her for much of my childhood and nothing would have stopped me from attending. BII did.*

During the last few years of implants, I suffered with severe depression. I didn't want to get out of bed. During the night, I didn't sleep. Crazy insomnia for years. The silence in the dark of night was spent wondering if I would live another day and the constant words "what is wrong with me". I spent years of my life feeling like I was in a drug induced stuper... I knew I was dying... and by the end of the illness, I wanted to. It's all I thought about. I wanted to be put out of this never ending nightmare. My arms, legs and feet would go so numb in the night that I could chop them off and not feel it. My legs would kick/ jerk out of control. It was awful.

This is not normal. I am in no way shape or form a hypochondriac.

10 days after my "light bulb" moment, I explanted (Dec 15, 2015). I went to another highly reviewed plastic surgeon in Florida for consult. I was so sick that I put in writing what I wanted to say at the consult because I knew I wouldn't be able to get the words out. He had never heard of BII but promised to remove my implants along with all of the capsules. The surgery was less than an hour and there was zero pain. I came into the surgery center that morning in a wheelchair in ridiculous joint pain. I told my husband and the surgeon if I didn't make it through the surgery, it was ok, I didn't want to spend another day on this planet suffering this way. The surgeon held my hands and we prayed to God to heal me. I walked out later that day already feeling better. I went back two or three days later for a post op and he and the entire staff were absolutely amazed the woman in front of them. I was putting sentences together, breathing, walking.. smiling and feeling hope for the first time in years. I was alive and it was nothing short of a miracle.

I asked about the capsules. He said "they were thin" and the body would absorb them. By this time, I knew better. Capsules do not get absorbed by our bodies. I immediately got another loan and scheduled an appointment out of state with a surgeon who knew how to remove the capsules. I wasn't going to take any chances because this new found feeling of being alive was something I longed for and I was not about to let it go. A few weeks later, my husband drove me 12 hours away and I had a 4 hour surgery to remove the capsules from my ribs and chest wall. That was a very painful procedure. But, I knew I was going to have my life back. I was right… I did.

No oxygen tank, no braces, no injections, no ER visits.. No more doctor appts since explant. I fully function, work full time and spend all of my free time helping a huge community of women that are sick with Breast Implant Illness. I receive hundreds of messages every week from women around the world who stumble across my Breast_ Implant_Illness page on Instagram.

I have said that I didn't get sick until year seven or eight but when looking back, I realize that it started much sooner but I contributed the symptoms to stress, motherhood, age, etc.

Diagnosis after diagnosis… there was always a reason for the many issues. The sad thing was, those issues never *got better even after numerous procedures, pokes, prods and piles of pharmaceuticals. It was seven or eight years until I realized that something was actually really wrong with me. It took that long to go through every possible medical profession and possible illness! It's infuriating that my life became this dark hole that I couldn't climb out of.*

I sit here now in 2021 writing this in tears. I'm pissed off that I lost so many years of my life.

We are told implants are safe and sadly many of us are deathly ill before we learn the truth.

They are not safe, never have been and never will be.

They are literally killing us.

This is why I work so hard to advocate for awareness. I cannot let my suffering go in vain. But I also hope the medical industry will take over and spread the word .. those of us that do this are entitled to have our lives back. To the naysayers, I don't spend every moment of my free time doing this because I have nothing better to do. I would cut off my right hand to have had the knowledge available that we share today. That is why I do it.

We often hear "BII symptoms are so across the board and could be anything" or "everyone deals with those symptoms from time to time" or "sounds like menopause" and my favorite "I have all that and I don't have implants". All BII victims have symptoms start with being occasional occurrences. As the years pass they grow to be every day, all day 24 x7.

Looking back, it's actually amazing how we believe everything our doctors tell us. They do not have a crystal ball unfortunately. They are expected to give us a diagnosis when we have a problem and get out the prescription pad to make it all better.

That's not what happens with a Breast Implant Illness patient… ever.. the prescription pad is an endless merry go round that only mask things for a very short time. It is not normal!"

'Having my implants removed was the best decision I ever made'

Mel Ward's Story:

In an Australian media outlet called Sunday Night, Mel Ward, a 37-year-old mother of two, shared her breast implant illness story at the time she had her breast implants removed. Now in her 40s and feeling very well again, she reflects on what was and became my on-line mentor as a mutual friend Dr Natalie Kringoudis put us in touch.

Mel shared the physical and mental changes she experienced after the operation with Sunday Night.

"At nine weeks post op from having the breast implants removed, my health results have been nothing short of dramatic, physically and mentally! Each day gets better and better. My energy is through the roof, to the point I've nearly forgotten how unwell I felt 24/7; how on God's earth I was walking around chronically ill astounds me today. I need to reflect on my list of symptoms to jog my memory!

The majority of the symptoms I carried for 10 years have gone. Most obvious is the chronic inflammation throughout my entire body. Since the brain fog has lifted my memory is sharper, and my anxiety and depression are gone (no medication for the past 12 weeks). The feelings of fatigue, blurred vision, muscle aches, joint aches, choking sensations, breathing difficulties and sinus pain are all gone. My eyes are both now the same size again. My uterus no longer feels as though I'm in labour, the frequent urination has subsided, my hair is growing, the finger nail ridges are smoothing out, the dark circles under my eyes are going, and the sensitivity I was experiencing to light and sound has gone.

My skin is clearing. I have regular bowel movements and my food intolerances have reduced. I've been eating super-clean albeit a few indulgent celebratory dinners, which haven't affected me the way they would have with toxic implants.

I will admit I went through a patch of confusion. I was so used to being sick, I didn't know how to start living in health. Being sick for nearly 10 years almost became my identity! But I've navigated my way through and I am feeling in control and super positive about the future. I'm living in the moment, being present for my daughters and my husband. Having my implants removed was the best decision I have ever made hands down!

Puffy / Before

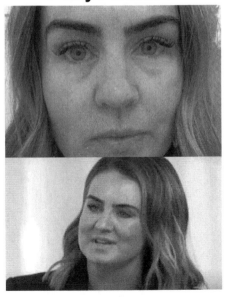

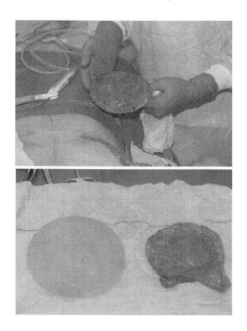

After

From breast cancer to explant advocate!

Robyn Towt's Story:

My name is Robyn Towt. I am a former school teacher and I have survived three cancers, most recently breast cancer in 2017. My experiences with cancer and my love for education have led me to become a patient advocate with a passion for research.

I stumbled into the world of advocacy after my breast cancer diagnosis. During that phase of my life, I was an active mom of two teenage boys, running the local high school basketball program in the east valley metropolitan Phoenix area. I grew up in Arizona and have always enjoyed many outdoor activities such as hiking, biking, golf, boating, waterskiing, wakeboarding and walking daily, usually an average of 5 miles per day.

When my cancer diagnosis came, my first thought was… "I don't have time for this." Our summers were always busy, traveling for basketball and trying to escape the Arizona summer heat. Breast cancer could not have come at a worse time for me. I had a bilateral mastectomy six days before my son's high school graduation. Surgery went well and thankfully I had an amazing support system of friends and family in my local community.

I wanted my breast cancer journey to be over with as quickly as possible so that I could enjoy my summer with my family. What followed after surgery became a very difficult endeavor for me. I struggled tremendously with the process of reconstruction surgery. There was no summer with my kids that year. I spent most days in bed or on the couch suffering from the pain that was caused by the tissue expanders, as well as other symptoms and health complications that had started developing. I had no idea that breast implants could cause me to experience health problems. I asked my doctors about the safety of breast implants, and I googled "are breast implants safe". Nothing scandalous came up so I continued on my reconstruction journey.

By the end of summer, I was so sick, experiencing over 20 debilitating symptoms and I could not get through the day without a nap. I had extreme fatigue and chronic pain, headaches/migraines, heart palpitations, rashes, hair loss, dizziness, joint and muscle pain, difficulty breathing and difficulty swallowing. I could not understand why I was experiencing these problems. I did not have chemotherapy or radiation treatments and I was not taking hormone inhibitors.

After four visits to my plastic surgeon, I ended up with four bottles of pills and still no answers. The symptoms worsened and I turned to an online breast cancer support group where I met a lady who shared her experience with Breast Implant Illness. When I heard her story and joined breast implant illness support groups online, I found an entire community of women who were experiencing the same complications from breast implants. Most of them were also not told about the risks of these systemic symptoms that are associated with breast implants. I had my implants removed after just four months and I completely regained my health and zest for life. I realized that this is an enormous women's health crisis and it didn't just happen to me, it's happening to hundreds of thousands of other women.

I started my advocacy journey in the breast implant illness support groups which led me to travel to Washington DC and share my testimony twice at the FDA. I also lobbied my state legislators to pass a state law in Arizona for surgeons to give patients proper informed consent for breast implant surgery and a patient decision checklist that I created, which includes all of the things that I wish I was told before having breast implant surgery. I am currently working on similar legislation in several other states. I also co-founded GPAC, the Global Patient Advocacy Coalition with my dear friend and fellow advocate Terri Diaz. We work with patient advocates all over the world to improve the standard of care for all patients and to raise awareness about medical device safety. We have regular meetings with the FDA, plastic surgeon societies, legislators, global health regulators, and state medical boards. Last year, we worked with the America Society of Plastic Surgeons (ASPS) to develop a patient decision checklist for breast implant surgery, which ASPS has adopted.

I have spent a lot of time researching the history of breast implants. After a 10 year ban on silicone breast implants in the early 1990's, the FDA allowed the breast implants to return to the market in 2006 under strict conditions that proper safety follow up was to be conducted. Each manufacturer was ordered to follow over 42,000 patients and monitor their health after having breast implant surgery. All manufacturers in the United States have violated their premarket approval agreements and the FDA was withholding over 446,000 reports of breast implant adverse events from the public[1,2,3,4,5,6]

In the past two decades, it has been discovered that breast implants cause multiple types of cancer [7,8,9] The first cases of these cancers were discovered in the early 1990's but they were not brought to the public until recently. The FDA and plastic surgery community have failed to alert the medical community about the dangers of breast implants and many patients suffer for longer than necessary because their doctors are unaware of the complications that are caused by breast implants[10-18] The FDA has posted alerts on their website and YouTube Channel, as well as sent communications to email subscribers, however their communications only reached a total of 320,500 people and there are almost 5 million practicing doctors and nurses currently in the United States.

PubMed®
Advanced   User Guide

Review

Silicone toxicology

H Busch. Semin Arthritis Rheum. 1994 Aug.

Show details   ⚙

🔲 **Full text links**   ❝ **Cite**   ...

Abstract

Silicone, a man-made polymer containing the element silicon, has been used in a variety of medical devices including breast implants. Silicone was used, in part, because it was suggested to have the property of biological inertness. Inert materials do not affect chemical, physiological, or immunological processes. Silicone is not inert. Silicone from breast implants "bleeds" through the surrounding envelope and is present in the surrounding capsule or migrates to other distant locations. Silicone and/or the multiple

As a patient advocate, I strive to use my experience and knowledge to help bridge the communication gap between patients and doctors, but most of all to ensure that the patient is the main focus and priority. I enjoy medical research and I have published articles in several magazines, as well as a medical journal and a medical textbook. I believe every patient should be given the information needed to make informed and educated decisions about their healthcare treatment and surgical options. When we know better, we must do better.

FDA STATEMENT

FDA Issues Safety Alert for Squamous Cell Carcinoma and Various Lymphomas in Scar Tissue around Breast Implants

The following statement is attributed to Binita Ashar, M.D., director of the Office of Surgical and Infection Control Devices in the FDA's Center for Devices and Radiological Health

Hey I wanted to let you know I have 2 female friends and 1 of them has implants and the other was thinking about getting them because she was recommending it to her. I didn't want to judge or say anything , but when I talked to my friend one on one and told her your story she reconsidered very quickly. Just thought you should know that your story inspired a close friend of mine to have more body positivity. 🤍

🖤

Amazing!

Hi andi, I just read the story about your explant breast surgery and I had the same experience. The MRI and doctors told me everything was fine but I knew something was wrong. $14000 later they are out and OBVIOUSLY ruptured and poisoning my body they were not fine! Keep talking and making it an issue - there are others out there like us!

Omg 💀 !!!! Wow! This needs to be highlighted. So sorry this happened to you.

Hey Andi, I've been following your breast explant journey and I must say I'm extremely surprised by the amount of breast tissue you have left. I have been following fb groups for explanting for a few years and I've never seen anyone end up with natural looking breasts? Do you mind if I ask if your implants were under or over the muscle?
Although I was a "C" size before I had my implants, I've been told that I would be a "AA" if I had them removed.
Thank you for sharing your amazing journey with everyone. You are a true blessing 🙏 🙇

View 1 previous reply

the_lil_black_dress_of_health 7h
@andi.lew totally. Size is discussed and shape is discussed. Protrusion, side boob, round or tear drop, saline or silicone. But nowhere at any time dis anyone tell me that my nipples would be cut out of my body and sat on a table beside me and then put back in and not work anymore. 🖤

1 like   Reply

Most relevant ˅

Kyla De Tracy Gould
Thanks so much for sharing this. I lost a lot of weight a few years ago and had wanted to get implants, but your post changed my mind. Not worth the risk thank you 🙏

40m   Like   Reply   Message   Hide   1

✏ Author
Andi Lew
Kyla De Tracy Gould oh my goodness. I'm so glad this made you change your mind. Breast implants are a ticking time bomb. They wreak havoc on your overall health and immune, digestive and nervous system. The whole system starts shutting down. You are beautiful exactly how you are!

prettyandi commented: 🖤 it's hard to see the raw beauty that is the "after" pic until you live the hard lesson. Vanity is heavy.. I carried it around for more than half my life. It's only when we free ourselves from this burden that we can see true beauty.
Explanted 3 years in May, after 18 years. 11m

References

1. https://www.who.int/news-room/facts-in-pictures/detail/breastfeeding#:~:text=Breastfeeding%20 for%20the%20first%20six%20months%20is%20 crucial&text=development%20and%20health%2C%20 and%20thereafter,to%20two%20years%20or%20beyond.

2. https://en.m.wikipedia.org/wiki/Hippocratic_Oath

3. https://journalofethics.ama-assn.org/article/silicone-breast-implant-litigation/2010-05

4. https://www.tga.gov.au/resources/publication/publications/consumer-fact-sheet-recall-allergan-biocell-breast-implants

5. https://www.nytimes.com/2008/02/21/washington/21device.htm

6. https://healthcare.utah.edu/the-scope/health-library/all/2019/05/do-women-breast-implants-have-higher-risk-of-cancer#:~:text=Jones%3A%20There%20are%20 about%20300%2C000,about%20risks%20and%20 side%20effects.

7. https://journalofethics.ama-assn.org/article/silicone-breast-implant-litigation/2010-05

8. https://www.newbeauty.com/ideal-implant-ceases-operations/?mibextid=Zxz2cZ

9. https://pubmed.ncbi.nlm.nih.gov/30820130/

10. Allergen pamphlet

11. Sientra Warning Letter 3/19/19 https://www.fda.gov/inspections-compliance-enforcement-and-criminal-investigations/warning-letters/sientra-inc-573436-03182019

12. Ideal Warning Letter 5/28/20 https://www.fda.gov/inspections-compliance-enforcement-and-criminal-investigations/warning-letters/ideal-implant-incorporated-606103-05142020

13. Allergan Warning Letter 5/28/20 https://www.fda.gov/inspections-compliance-enforcement-and-criminal-investigations/warning-letters/allergan-607690-05142020

14. Mentor Warning Letter 3/19/19 https://www.fda.gov/inspections-compliance-enforcement-and-criminal-investigations/warning-letters/mentor-worldwide-llc-acclarent-573520-03182019

15. FDA Hidden Reports https://www.azfamily.com/news/investigations/breast_implant_illness_investigation/decoded-fda-data-dump-reveals-medical-devices-with-most-reported/article_49e1eee4-cebf-11e9-9859-ffca4492b9b6.html

16. FDA Hidden Reports https://www.icij.org/investigations/implant-files/fda-kept-hundreds-of-thousands-of-breast-implant-fbclid=IwAR24r4HVFAfKZSKKIcPBLWSk8z5dZwDIET0GUaXoS3oy4vsJkE3MVnPm2Pwincidents-hidden-from-public/?

17. FDA statement BIA-ALCL https://www.fda.gov/medical-devices/breast-implants/medical-device-reports-breast-implant-associated-anaplastic-large-cell-lymphoma

18. FDA statement BIA-SCC and Other Cancers https://www.fda.gov/news-events/press-announcements/fda-issues-safety-alert-squamous-cell-carcinoma-and-various-lymphomas-scar-tissue-around-breast

19. ASPS statement on Breast Implant Cancers https://www.plasticsurgery.org/for-medical-professionals/publications/psn-extra/news/asps-statement-on-breast-implant-associated-squamous-cell-carcinoma

SCC Publications

20. https://www.researchgate.net/figure/a-Pre-operative-marking-of-left-ALT-flap-b-Post-operative-donor-site-closed-by-primary_fig4_332276757

21. https://www.plasticsurgery.org/for-medical-professionals/publications/psn-extra/news/asps-statement-on-breast-implant-associated-squamous-cell-carcinoma

22. https://journals.lww.com/annalsplasticsurgery/abstract/1992/11000/squamous_cell_carcinoma_following_breast.9.aspx

23. https://pubmed.ncbi.nlm.nih.gov/28739500/

24. https://pubmed.ncbi.nlm.nih.gov/32804719/

25. https://www.cancerjournal.net/article.asp?issn=0973-1482;year=2019;volume=15;issue=5;spage=1057;epage=1061;aulast=Soliman

26. Breast implant capsule-associated squamous cell carcinoma: a report of 2 cases - PubMed

ALCL Publications

27. https://www.citizen.org/article/letter-on-inaccurate-communications-regarding-risks-of-breast-implant-related-cancer/

28. https://www.ncbi.nlm.nih.gov/pmc/articles/PMC9508381/

Resources

CBH Energetics
Need detox support?

CBH Energetics is an advanced 'at home' health testing kit, empowering you to assess your bioenergetic health conveniently and accurately and follow up with natural health practitioners. The cutting edge technology supports you in understanding your wellbeing from a holistic and bio-individual perspective

www.CBHenergetics.com

3ifulvic
Fulvic acid and humic acid are helpful for heavy metal detoxing
www.3ifulvic.com

Mast Cell Activation Syndrome Support
www.mastcell360.com
for the recommended diet and castor oil packs

Hallstein Water
www.hallsteinwater.com
Use my code ANDI25

Bubble and Bee
A USDA Certified Organic body care product brand that can help you live a toxic free life
www.bubbleandbee.com

andilew.com
For more learning and coaching

Aires Tech
Feeling sensitive to EMF/EMR? Electromagnetic radiation may exacerbate breast implants illness symptoms. Aires Tech products may help modulate the radiation emitted.
Use my code Andi25

www.AiresTech.com

Testimonial by Pinky Mckay,

best-selling author and lactation consultant.

"This is such a courageous book, that will open the hornet's nest for many women about body image, life choices, perceptions of beauty and cultural pressures and influences, as well as how some parts of the medical industry isn't always about 'doing no harm'."

Listen to Andi's show on

Spotify, Apple or wherever you get your podcast!

It's the podcast that introduces you to the most up to date wellness people, brands and businesses.

Andi interviews guests who are abundant in wellness, love and service, from all over the world. Be inspired as they share what they do to create optimal function and health.